Dragons, Jungles and Dinosaurs
ANTHOLOGY

Gill & Macmillan
Hume Avenue
Park West
Dublin 12
www.gillmacmillan.ie

ISBN: 9780717152988
© John Hartnett, Eithne Kennedy, Patricia O'Doherty, Eileen Phelan 2012

Design: Aisli Madden / Outburst Design
Cover Illustration: Aisli Madden
Inside Illustrations: MSM Studios
Printed by Edelvives, Spain

First Published March 2012

The paper used in this book is made from the wood pulp of managed forests. For every tree felled, at least one tree is planted, thereby renewing natural resources.

Dear Reader,

Welcome to *Dragons, Jungles and Dinosaurs*. This anthology is filled with a wide range of interesting fiction, poetry and non-fiction pieces. We hope you have as much fun reading this selection, as we had in putting it together.

The fiction includes extracts from lots of different kinds of stories: funny ones, sad ones, fantasies, mysteries, as well as picture books and classics. We hope that if you really like an author or a story you will go on to read the entire novel and find other titles in that genre or by the same author.

Within the non-fiction, there is a variety of pieces, from information to instruction to puzzles. You can read about topics that link up with some of the fiction themes. For example, after the story *Dino Egg*, you can find out all about dinosaurs. Then there are pieces relating to the kinds of reading you may have to do in order to locate information or to complete a task, e.g. how to read a chart or crack a code. These pieces have lots of photographs, tables, maps and headings to help you learn about the topic.

As well as introducing you to a range of genres, this book is designed to help you boost your reading skills and develop the strategies that good readers use. There are 'before reading', 'during reading' and 'after reading' questions or prompts to help you along the way. Let's take a look at some of these special features.

Before reading:

Think of this as a warm-up activity for reading. It is about getting your mind ready to read the text. We may ask you to make predictions about what you imagine the text will be about by checking the title, examining the artwork or photographs, scanning and reading headings, or considering what you already know about the topic or the author's style of writing.

> 1. Look closely at the artwork. Describe what you think is happening.
> 2. Have you read books or seen movies about children who are horrid or unpleasant? Talk about them.
>
> ## Horrid Henry

During reading:

Notice the little stars on the page. These are a signal to you to check out the prompt or question in the coloured box at the end of the page before you read on. It is also a signal to slow down your reading and to ponder

> terrible deed you like. Horrid Henry was sure to have done it. ⭑
> Horrid Henry had a younger brother. His name was Perfect Peter.
> Perfect Peter always said 'please' and
>
> ⭑ Think of some other terrible deeds that Henry might have done.
>
> 12

this important element of the story. We might ask you to notice how the author creates a mood or how a character is feeling or why they reacted to a particular event in the story.

After reading (fiction):

Notice the icons on the left-hand side. They are a signal to you that you have to think differently in order to answer the question.

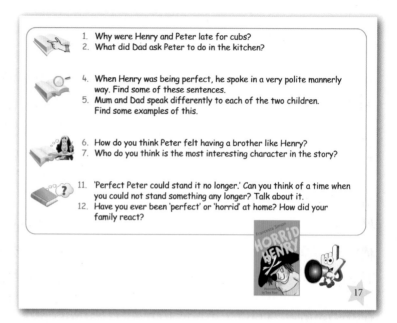

1. Why were Henry and Peter late for cubs?
2. What did Dad ask Peter to do in the kitchen?

4. When Henry was being perfect, he spoke in a very polite mannerly way. Find some of these sentences.
5. Mum and Dad speak differently to each of the two children. Find some examples of this.

6. How do you think Peter felt having a brother like Henry?
7. Who do you think is the most interesting character in the story?

11. 'Perfect Peter could stand it no longer.' Can you think of a time when you could not stand something any longer? Talk about it.
12. Have you ever been 'perfect' or 'horrid' at home? How did your family react?

17

These questions ask you to recall details from the story. There is only one right answer and you can find it in one particular spot in the story.

These questions also ask you to recall some details from the story. The answer is in the text but you will have to find it in different parts of the story and put it all together to respond correctly. This section may also draw attention to particular words or phrases in the story.

These questions ask you to read between the lines. This means the question cannot be answered directly from the text and there is no one right answer. These questions are great 'conversation starters'. You may also find your answer or opinion differs to that of your classmates. You will need to back up your answer with evidence from the text, so you may have to re-read parts of the story and think deeply about these questions.

These questions also relate to the story but go beyond it. The answer is not in the text. In fact, you could answer the question without having read the text. They are 'real world' questions that may ask you to think about the theme of the story or a particular topic or issue. These too are great 'conversation starters'.

At the end of each extract, we have (where possible) included the cover of the book it was taken from and earmarked if an audio recording of this extract is available on our website: www.fireworksenglish.ie

So happy reading, thinking and debating... go have some fun; lose yourself in a story, a poem or discover something new in an information piece.

Contents

An Irish giant

1. Do you know any stories about giants? Talk about them in class.
2. Look at the artwork. Say what you think is happening in each picture.

About 200 years ago in Ireland there was a man called Patrick Cotter O'Brien. Patrick was an ordinary man, except for one thing. He was very tall. In fact, Patrick was nearly three metres tall.

People came from all over the country just to look at him. Some had to climb up on tables and chairs just to reach the top of his head.

Patrick worked as a builder. When he was building a house, he didn't really need a ladder. He just stood on tiptoe.

But Patrick was very poor. So he decided to go to London to seek his fortune. Soon he became very famous. Everyone came to see the Irish giant. People even paid money to see him and soon Patrick was very rich.

Patrick was a very shy person and sometimes he would not go out during the day because he was worried that people would stare at him. Instead, Patrick liked to walk around the streets of London at night. He often stopped to light his pipe from a gas lamp.

As Patrick got older, he found it hard to walk. So he decided to buy a coach. But he couldn't get one big enough. He had to have a special coach made. A big box was fixed beneath the coach to make room for his legs. One day a highwayman tried to rob Patrick's coach. You can imagine his shock when Patrick put his head out the window. The highwayman was so terrified he galloped off empty-handed.

When Patrick Cotter O'Brien died, carpenters had to make a special giant coffin for him. Patrick was afraid that people would try to dig up his body when he was dead. He gave orders that his coffin should be lined with lead and put into a grave made out of solid rock! Iron bars were then laid across the coffin. When he died it took 14 men to lower him into the ground.

People said that Patrick kept a diary of his life but it seems that he burnt it and none of it remains today.

1. Do you think Patrick had a happy life? Why? Talk about it.
2. Imagine you are Patrick. Describe a day in your life.
3. Draw a chart showing the heights of the children in your class.
4. Do you know any facts about giants in the world of nature? You can find out more on pages 84-87.

This picture of Patrick with his tailor was drawn by John Kay, Patrick's barber.

1. What might this story be about? Use the title and pictures to help you predict.
2. Read the first paragraph silently. What could the secret be?
3. Have you read stories or seen films about giants? Talk about them.

The Little Boy's Secret

David L. Harrison

One day a little boy left school early because he had a secret to tell his mother. He was in a hurry to get home, so he took a short cut through some woods where three terrible giants lived.

He hadn't gone far before he met one of them standing in the path.

When the giant saw the little boy, he put his hands on his hips and roared, 'What are you doing here, boy? Don't you know whose woods these are?'

'I'm on my way home,' answered the little boy. 'I have a secret to tell my mother.'

That made the giant furious. 'Secret?' he bellowed. 'What secret?'

'I can't tell you,' said the little boy, 'or it wouldn't be a secret any more.'

Do you think the little boy is afraid of the giant? How do you know?

'Then I'm taking you to our castle!' said the giant. Stooping down, he picked up the little boy and popped him into his shirt pocket. Before long the first giant met a second giant who was twice as big, three times as ugly, and four times as fierce.

'What's that in your pocket?' he asked the first giant.

'A boy,' he answered. 'Says he has a secret that he won't tell us.'

When the second giant heard that, he laughed a wicked laugh. 'Won't tell us, eh?' he chuckled. 'Well, we'll just see about that! To the castle with him!'

The giants thumped on down the path. In a short time they came to a huge stone castle beside a muddy river.

At the door they met the third giant, who was five times bigger, six times uglier, and seven times fiercer than the second giant.

'What's that in your pocket?' he asked the first giant.

'A boy,' he answered.

'A boy!' chuckled the third giant. He brought his face close to the pocket and peered in.

'He has a secret he won't tell us,' said the first giant.

When the third giant heard that he laughed a terrible laugh.

'Won't tell us, eh?' he asked. 'Well, we'll just see about that! On the table with him!'

The first giant took the little boy from his pocket and put him on the kitchen table.

⭐ What might the third giant look like?

5

Then all three giants gathered round and peered down at him.

The little boy looked at the first giant. He looked at the second giant. He looked at the third giant. They were truly enormous and dreadful to behold.

'Well?' said the first giant.

'We're waiting,' said the second giant.

'I'll count to three,' said the third giant. 'One... two...'

The little boy sighed a big sigh.

'Oh, all right,' he said. 'I suppose I can tell you. But if I do, you must promise to let me go.'

'We promise,' answered the giants. But they all winked sly winks at one another and crossed their fingers behind their backs because they didn't really mean to let him go at all.

The little boy turned to the first giant. 'Bend down,' he said. The giant leaned down and the little boy whispered into his ear.

When the giant heard the secret, he leaped up from the table. His knees shook. His tongue hung out.

'Oh, no!' he shouted. 'That's terrible!' And he dashed from the castle, ran deep into the woods, and climbed to the top of a tall tree. He didn't come down for three days.

The second giant scowled at the little boy.

'What's wrong with him?' he asked.

'Never mind,' said the little boy. 'Just bend down.'

The second giant leaned down and the little boy stood on his toes and whispered into his ear.

When the giant heard the secret, he leaped up so fast he knocked his chair over. His eyes rolled. His ears twitched. 'I have to get away,' he roared. He raced from the castle into the hills and crawled into the deepest, darkest cave he could find.

The third giant frowned down at the little boy.

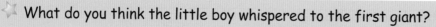

What do you think the little boy whispered to the first giant?

'What's wrong with them?' he asked.

'Never mind,' said the little boy. 'Just bend down.'

The giant leaned down and the little boy climbed on to a teacup and whispered into his ear.

When the giant heard the secret, he jumped up so fast that he ripped the seat of his trousers. His teeth chattered. His hair stood on end. 'Help!' he cried. 'Help!'

And he dashed from the castle and dived head first into the muddy river.

The castle door had been left open, and since the giants had promised the little boy that he could go, he walked out and went home.

At last he was able to tell his mother his secret; but she didn't yell and run away. She just put him to bed and gave him some supper.

The next morning when the little boy woke up, he was covered from head to toe with bright red spots.

'Now I can tell *everybody* what my secret was,' he said with a smile. 'My secret was... I'M GETTING THE MEASLES!'

1. Why did the boy take a shortcut through the woods?
2. Where did the third giant go when he heard the secret?

3. Find all the words which show how the giants moved and spoke.
4. What did each giant do when he heard the secret? Which do you think was the funniest reaction?
5. This story is very far-fetched. What parts of it are hardest to believe?

6. Were you surprised by the ending?
7. Can you think of a different secret or a different ending for this story?
8. If the little boy had been afraid of the giants how would the story have been different?
9. If there was a fourth giant how do you think he would be described?
10. Imagine the conversation between the little boy and his mum when he got home. Act it out with your friend for the class.

11. What would you do if you met a giant?
12. What is your favourite fairytale? Talk about it.
13. Talk about secrets. Are there times when it's good to keep a secret? Are there times when it's bad to keep a secret?

The Book of
GIANT STORIES
by David L. Harrison

Illustrated by Philippe Fix

My Baby Brother's Secret

John Foster

When my baby brother
wants to tell me a secret,
He comes right up close.
But instead of putting his lips
against my ear,
he presses his ear
tightly against my ear.
Then, he whispers so softly
that I can't hear
a word he's saying.

My baby brother's secrets
are safe with me.

1. Do you like this poster? Why?
2. Have you ever been to a circus, pantomime or magic show? Talk about it.

See www.greatestshow.ie for more details of this amazing show.

The greatest show in the world

Featuring Mr Pepper's Amazing Acrobats

- High-flying trapeze
- Jugglers
- Magicians
- Human cannonball

See belly and limbo dancers, tight-rope walkers, fire-eaters, high wire acts, death-defying stunts and crazy clowns.

FOR ONE WEEK ONLY

The greatest show in the world

Featuring Mr Pepper's Amazing Acrobats

TICKET

This ticket admits one child only
Valid for 3rd July

Turn this ticket over for address and other details. This ticket is not refundable.

Time: 5.30 – 7.30pm
Cost: €6.00

Over fifty superb acts! Fun for all the family! Mr Pepper's show with more superstars than ever before.

Watch Ivan the Incredible and his magicians create dazzling magic tricks.

All the way from Spain, Señor Mendes will ride his bike across a high wire.

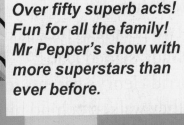

Show times:
3rd – 9th July,
Monday to Saturday 5.30 – 7.30pm
Sunday 4.00 – 6.00pm

Adults   €12.00
Children €6.00

1. How many acts are mentioned in the poster? What other acts might you see?
2. How much would it cost for your family to go to the show?
3. Design your own poster for a circus, pantomime or magic show.

1. Look closely at the artwork. Describe what you think is happening.
2. Have you read books or seen movies about children who are horrid or unpleasant? Talk about them.

Horrid Henry

Francesca Simon

Henry was horrid.

Everyone said so, even his mother.

Henry threw food, Henry snatched, Henry pushed and shoved and pinched.

Even his teddy avoided him when possible. His parents despaired.

'What are we going to do about that horrid boy?' sighed Mum.

'How did two people as nice as us have such a horrid child?' sighed Dad.

When Horrid Henry's parents took Henry to school they walked behind him and pretended he was not theirs.

Children pointed at Henry and whispered to their parents,

'That's Horrid Henry.'

'He's the boy who threw my jacket in the mud.'

'He's the boy who squashed Billy's beetle.'

'He's the boy who ...' Fill in whatever terrible deed you like. Horrid Henry was sure to have done it.

Horrid Henry had a younger brother. His name was Perfect Peter.

Perfect Peter always said 'please' and

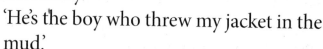
Think of some other terrible deeds that Henry might have done.

'thank you'. Perfect Peter loved vegetables.
Perfect Peter always used a hankie and never, ever picked his nose.
'Why can't you be perfect like Peter?' said Henry's Mum every day.

As usual, Henry pretended not to hear. He continued melting Peter's crayons on the radiator.
But Horrid Henry started to think.
'What if I were perfect?' thought Henry. 'I wonder what would happen.'
When Henry woke the next morning, he did not wake Peter by pouring water on Peter's head.

Peter did not scream.
This meant Henry's parents overslept and Henry and Peter were late for Cubs.
Henry was very happy.
Peter was very sad to be late for Cubs.
But because he was perfect, Peter did not whine or complain.
On the way to Cubs, Henry did not squabble with Peter over who sat in front. He did not pinch Peter and he did not shove Peter.
Back home, when Perfect Peter built a castle, Henry did not knock it down. Instead, Henry sat on the sofa and read a book.

Mum and Dad ran into the room.
'It's awfully quiet in here,' said Mum. 'Are you being horrid, Henry?'
'No,' said Henry.
'Peter, is Henry knocking your castle down?'
Peter longed to say 'yes'. But that would be a lie.

13

'No,' said Peter.

He wondered why Henry was behaving so strangely.

'What are you doing, Henry?' said Dad.

'Reading a wonderful story about some super mice,' said Henry.

Dad had never seen Henry read a book before.

He checked to see if a comic was hidden inside.

There was no comic. Henry was actually reading a book.

'Hmmmmn,' said Dad.

It was almost time for dinner. Henry was hungry and went into the kitchen where Dad was cooking.

But instead of shouting, 'I'm starving! Where's my food?' Henry said, 'Dad, you look tired. Can I help get supper ready?'

'Don't be horrid, Henry,' said Dad, pouring peas into boiling water. Then he stopped.

'What did you say, Henry?' asked Dad.

'Can *I* help, Dad?' said Perfect Peter.

'I asked if you needed any help,' said Henry.

'I asked first,' said Peter.

'Henry will just make a mess,' said Dad. 'Peter, would you peel the carrots while I sit down for a moment?'

'Of course,' said Perfect Peter.

Peter washed his spotless hands.

Peter put on his spotless apron.

Peter rolled up his spotless sleeves.

Peter waited for Henry to snatch the peeler. But Henry laid the table instead. Mum came into the kitchen.

'Smells good,' she said. 'Thank you, darling Peter, for laying the table. What a good boy you are.'

Peter did not say anything.

'I laid the table, Mum,' said Henry.

Mum stared at him.

'You?' said Mum.

'Me,' said Henry.

'Why?' said Mum.

Henry smiled.

'To be helpful,' he said.

'You've done something horrid, haven't you, Henry?' said Dad.

'No,' said Henry. He tried to look sweet.

'I'll lay the table tomorrow,' said Perfect Peter.

'Thank you, angel,' said Mum.

'Dinner is ready,' said Dad.

'You're very quiet tonight, Henry,' said Dad.

'The better to enjoy my lovely dinner,' said Henry.

'Henry, where are your peas and carrots?' asked Mum.

'I ate them,' said Henry. 'They were delicious.'

Mum looked on the floor. She looked under Henry's chair. She looked under his plate.

'You ate your peas and carrots?' said Mum slowly.

She felt Henry's forehead.

'Are you feeling all right, Henry?'

'Yeah,' said Horrid Henry. 'I'm fine, thank you for asking,' he added quickly.

Mum and Dad looked at each other. What was going on?

How do you think Henry feels here?

Henry's parents had been suspicious of him before now. Find some examples.

Then they looked at Henry.
'Henry, come here and let me
give you a big kiss,' said Mum.
'You are a wonderful boy.
Would you like a piece of fudge
cake?'

Peter interrupted.
'No cake for me, thank you,'
said Peter. 'I would rather have more vegetables.'
Henry let himself be kissed. Oh my, it was hard work being perfect.
He smiled sweetly at Peter.
'I would love some cake, thank you,' said Henry.
Perfect Peter could stand it no longer. He
picked up his plate and aimed it at Henry.
Then Peter threw the spaghetti.
Henry ducked.
SPLAT!
Spaghetti landed on Mum's head. Tomato
sauce trickled down her neck and down her
new pink fuzzy jumper.
'PETER!!!' yelled Mum and Dad.
'YOU HORRID BOY!' yelled Mum.
'GO TO YOUR ROOM!!' yelled Dad.
Perfect Peter burst into tears and ran to his
room.
Mum wiped
spaghetti off
her face.
She looked
very funny.
Henry tried
not to laugh.
He squeezed
his lips together tightly.

But it was no use. I am sorry to say that he could not stop a laugh escaping.
'It's not funny!' shouted Dad.
'Go to your room!' shouted Mum.
But Henry didn't care.
Who would have thought being perfect would be such fun?

1. Why were Henry and Peter late for Cubs?
2. What did Dad ask Peter to do in the kitchen?
3. Why did the spaghetti land on Mum's head?

4. When Henry was being perfect, he spoke in a very polite mannerly way. Find some of these sentences.
5. Mum and Dad speak differently to each of the two children. Find some examples of this.

6. How do you think Peter felt having a brother like Henry?
7. Who do you think is the most interesting character in the story?
8. How would you have responded if you were Henry's parents?
9. Imagine what happened next.
10. Tell the story from the point of view of Henry's Mum and Dad.

11. 'Perfect Peter could stand it no longer.' Can you think of a time when you could not stand something any longer? Talk about it.
12. Have you ever been 'perfect' or 'horrid' at home? How did your family react?

Birthdays around the world

⭐ What do you like to do on your birthday?

On your birthday, you probably like to get presents from your family and friends and have a delicious birthday cake with a candle for every year. Perhaps everyone sings 'Happy Birthday', then you blow out your candles and make a wish. These are birthday traditions in Ireland. In other countries people have very different customs.

Denmark: Flying flags
A flag is flown outside the window of the birthday house. During the night, presents are placed around the bed of the birthday boy or girl. In the morning he or she will find them.

Mexico: Piñatas
A piñata is a big hollow papier-mâché ball or shape. It is filled with sweets or other goodies and hung from the ceiling. The birthday child is blindfolded and strikes the piñata with a stick. When the piñata is cracked open all the goodies shower down and are shared.

Ireland: Birthday bumps
The birthday child is lifted by two friends, one holding the feet, the other holding the arms. He or she is lifted up and bumped very gently on the floor, one bump for each year and one extra bump for good luck!

Nigeria: Food celebration
The 1st, 5th, 10th and 15th birthdays are very special events. On these birthdays a party is held, often with up to 100 guests. A special dish is served: rice with tomatoes, red peppers, onions and cassava (which is like a sweet potato.)

Argentina: Pulls on the earlobe
The birthday child gets pulled on the earlobe, one pull for each year.

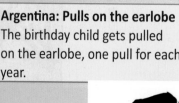

Do you know how to say Happy Birthday in another language?

- Lá Breithe Shona Dhuit
- Feliz Cumpleaños
- Fröhlicher Geburtstag

1. Make a birthday chart of your class. In which month do most children have a birthday?
2. What do you like to do to make your birthday special? Are there other birthday traditions in your class?
3. Design a birthday card.

Lithuania: Colourful garland
A colourful garland is hung around the door of the birthday person's home. The birthday boy or girl also sits in a decorated chair and family members lift them three times.

China: Noodles for lunch
The birthday child bows to his or her parents and receives a gift of money. Friends and relations are invited to lunch and noodles are served to wish the birthday child a long life.

Poland: Name days
In Poland and many other countries, children are called after saints and their name-day is celebrated more than the date of their birth. For example Polish children called Józef (Joseph) will celebrate their name-day on March 19 every year, the feast-day of St. Joseph. Polish people wish each other 'Sto lat!' which means 'One hundred years!'

Japan: New clothes
The birthday child receives an entirely new outfit to mark the occasion.

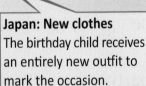

New Zealand: Birthday claps
After the birthday candles are lit on the cake, the happy birthday song is sung loudly and then the guests clap - one clap for each year the birthday person has been alive and one for good luck.

Israel: Chair raising
The birthday child sits in a chair while grown-ups lift and lower it a number of times, one for each year of the child's life.

At My Birthday Party

Anthony Browne

At my birthday party
I had chocolate cake,
And cheesecake,
And fruitcake,
And ginger cake,
And fudge cake.
After that I had stummer cake.

Happy Dogday

Peter Dixon

Today –
Is our dog's birthday.

It's Happydogdayday.
Sixteen years of panting
And sixteen years of play.

Sixteen years of dogtime.
Sixteen years of barks
– eating smelly dog food
And making muddy marks.

It's a hundred years of our time
It's a hundred human years
– of digging in the garden
and scratching itchy ears.

It's a hundred years of living rooms
(he never goes upstairs)
and dropping hairy whiskers
and being pushed off chairs...

It's a hundred years of being with us
A hundred years of Dad…
and a hundred of my sister
(that must be really bad!)

So:

No wonder he looks really old
No wonder he is grey
And cannot hear
Or jump
Or catch
Or even run away...
No wonder that he sleeps all day,
No wonder that he's fat
And only dreams of catching things
and chasing neighbours' cats...

So fight your fights
In dogdream nights
Deep within your bed...

today's your day
and we all say...

HAPPY BIRTHDAY FRED

21

1. Read the title and look at the pictures. Do you think this is a true story? Why?
2. Look closely at the pictures. What do you think is happening in each one?

Sunkaissa the Golden-haired Princess

Michael Rosen

Sunkaissa the Golden-haired Princess is a traditional tale from Nepal. It is retold by Michael Rosen.

Once long ago, in the mountains, a huge and horrible monster fell in love with a golden-haired princess called Sunkaissa. He watched her going about her work and one day, when she was out working, he seized her and took her off to his cave higher up the mountain. Sunkaissa's family were overcome with despair and sadness that they had lost their beautiful girl.

But her eldest brother was a brave young man and he said, 'Listen, we'll never get her back sitting round here crying. I'm going to go up the mountain and find her.'

'No,' said his father, 'the monster has taken her. You're no match for him. He'll tear you apart with one blow. Isn't it bad enough that we've lost a daughter? We don't want to lose a son as well.'

But the young man wouldn't listen.

'I can't sit here, knowing that the monster has her in his clutches. I'd rather die than put up with it.'

Would you have listened to the father? Why?

22

Off he went, up, up the mountain, but there was no sign of his sister. He crossed right over the top down on to the other side; he crossed valleys, rivers, forests, but never a sign of the monster or Sunkaissa. Then one day, he was sitting by a stream when he glanced down and saw, there in the grass, some long golden hairs. Surely these must belong to Sunkaissa, he thought. If I follow the stream I'll find her.

Off he went, following the stream, looking out for signs. Then, glancing up from the ground, he caught sight of a great dark cave in the rocks. He hid behind a tree and watched and waited. It wasn't long before a young woman with long golden hair came out. She sat down on the grass and started combing her hair. It was Sunkaissa. Her brother crept closer to her not wanting to surprise her and make her call out. Just as he was close by, she dropped her comb.

And as she did this, she said, without so much as a glance up at the person who had made a shadow on the ground beside her, 'Please pick up my comb for me.'

Her brother picked up the comb and handed it to her, but he could see that

Sunkaissa didn't know him or recognise him. So he sang to her a song with a tune that they had sung together when they were young:

'I am your brother, one of your own,
I've travelled the mountains to find you,
I've looked in the fields, I've looked by the streams,
And now I've found you, you can come home.'

It could have been the words, it could have been the tune – Sunkaissa now recognised her brother. And she was frightened.

'I can't come, dear brother. The monster will catch us and tear us to bits.'

'Well, hide me somewhere near so that I can have time to think how we can get rid of the monster.'

'You can hide in the cowshed,' said Sunkaissa. 'In there is a cow. Nothing like one you've ever seen

before. Enormous. Gigantic. When she moos, jump into her mouth and hide. Go now, quickly, before the monster comes back.'

The brother dashed off to the cowshed and there was the biggest cow the world has ever seen. He climbed up on to a beam and when the cow mooed, he jumped into its mouth. And there he sat till the evening.

Suddenly there came a great shaking of the ground and a great roaring in the air. The door of the cowshed crashed open and there stood the monster.

How do you know that Sunkaissa's brother cared for her?

'I smell the smell of a human being,' he roared.

'No,' said the cow. 'You've got it wrong. There's no human being in here.'

'Don't lie to me, cow,' said the monster. 'When I say there's a human being in here, then there's a human being.'

'Well now,' said the cow, 'I tell you what. I've always wanted to know how many hairs there are on my body. If you could count all the hairs on my body then I might be able to find a human being for you.'

'Very well,' growled the monster and he started counting. This shouldn't take me long, he thought.

'1, 2, 3... 234... 8976... one million... (the hours were passing, the monster's eyes were beginning to get tired but on he went)... two million... three million, three million and one...'

Just then the cow shivered. A great big shaky shiver and the monster lost his place.

'I don't know where I was!' he shouted.

'Oh really?' said the cow. 'I'm so sorry. Don't worry, start again and I'm sure you'll get it right next time.'

The monster started again and this time he got to four million and nineteen when the cow gave another great shaky shiver and the monster lost his place again. Well, this went on for hours and hours. Every time the monster got anywhere near counting all the hairs, the cow shivered. Little by little, the monster began to get tired. His head drooped and he started to mutter.

'Three milly, four humble, bendy boo tousled, two humble and bendy tree; three milly, four humble, bendy boo tousled, two humble and bendy floor; three milly, four humble, bendy boo –' and he flopped to the floor fast asleep.

Out of the cow's mouth jumped the brother.

He leapt onto the monster and killed him. Then he ran to find Sunkaissa and together they made the long journey home. You can imagine how overjoyed their family and the people of the village were to see them, and how they loved hearing the story of the cow.

And you know, if you watch a cow, you can see to this day that, whether she's in the field or the cowshed, every ten minutes or so she gives a shaky shiver.

> Why do you think the cow really asked the monster to count the hairs on its body?

25

1. Why were Sunkaissa's parents very sad?
2. Why did Sunkaissa's father not want her brother to search for her?
3. How did the monster know that Sunkaissa's brother was in the shed?

4. What words would you use to describe Sunkaissa's eldest brother?
5. How was the cow unlike any other cow?
6. How do you know that Sunkaissa was used to being treated like a princess?

7. In what other way might this story have ended?
8. Which part of the story is most unbelievable? Why do you think this?

9. Can you remember any song or tune from when you were younger?
10. Think of other stories where the hero kills a monster. Talk about them.
11. Do you know any other tales from around the world?

1. Read the title and look closely at the pictures. Make a prediction about the story.
2. What do you know about whales?
3. Do you think whales can sing?

The Whales' Song

Dyan Sheldon and Gary Blythe

Lilly's grandmother told her a story. 'Once upon a time,' she said, 'the ocean was filled with whales. They were as big as the hills. They were as peaceful as the moon. They were the most wondrous creatures you could ever imagine.'
Lilly climbed on to her grandmother's lap.
'I used to sit at the end of the jetty and listen for whales,' said Lilly's grandmother. 'Sometimes I'd sit there all day and all night. Then all of a sudden I'd see them coming from miles away. They moved through the water as if they were dancing.'
'But how did they know you were there, Grandma?' asked Lilly. 'How would they find you?'
Lilly's grandmother smiled. 'Oh, you had to bring them something special. A perfect shell. Or a beautiful stone. And if they liked you the whales would take your gift and give you something in return.'
'What would they give you, Grandma?' asked Lilly. 'What did you get from the whales?'
Lilly's grandmother sighed. 'Once or twice,' she whispered, 'once or twice I heard them sing.'

How do we know that Grandma loved the whales?

27

Lilly's uncle Frederick stomped into the room.

'You're nothing but a daft old fool!' he snapped. 'Whales were important for their meat, and for their bones, and for their blubber. If you have to tell Lilly something, then tell her something useful. Don't fill her head with nonsense. Singing whales indeed!'

'There were whales here millions of years before there were ships, or cities, or even cavemen,' continued Lilly's grandmother. 'People used to say they were magical.'

'People used to eat them and boil them down for oil!' grumbled Lilly's uncle Frederick. And he turned his back and stomped out to the garden.

Lilly dreamt about whales.

In her dreams she saw them, as large as mountains and bluer than the sky. In her dreams she heard them singing, their voices like the wind. In her dreams they leapt from the water and called her name. Next morning Lilly went down to the ocean.

She went where no one fished or swam or sailed their boats. She walked to the end of the old jetty, the water  was empty and still. Out of her pocket she took a yellow flower and dropped it into the water.

'This is for you,' she called into the air.

Lilly sat at the end of the jetty and waited.

She waited all morning and all afternoon.

Then, as dusk began to fall, Uncle Frederick came down the hill after her.

> Have you noticed a change in the mood of the story? What words helped to change the mood?

'Enough of this foolishness,' he said. 'Come on home. I'll not have you dreaming your life away.'

That night, Lilly awoke suddenly. The room was bright with moonlight. She sat up and listened. The house was quiet. Lilly climbed out of bed and went to the window. She could hear something in the distance, on the far side of the hill. She raced outside and down to the shore.

Her heart was pounding as she reached the sea.

There, enormous in the ocean, were the whales.

They leapt and jumped and spun across the moon.

Their singing filled up the night.

Lilly saw her yellow flower dancing on the spray.

Minutes passed, or maybe hours. Suddenly Lilly felt the breeze rustle her nightdress and the cold nip at her toes. She shivered and rubbed her eyes. Then it seemed the ocean was still again and the night black and silent.

Lilly thought she must have been dreaming. She stood up and turned for home. Then from far, far away, on the breath of the wind she heard,

'Lilly!

Lilly!'

The whales were calling her name.

1. What did Lilly's grandma give to the whales?
2. Where did Lilly's grandmother sit to listen for the whales?
3. What gift did Lilly have for the whales?

4. Compare Uncle Frederick's and Grandma's views of the whales.
5. What kind of character is a.) Grandma b.) Lilly?
6. What words are used in the story to describe the whales?

7. Do you think Lilly was dreaming? Say why.
8. Do you think Lilly will tell about what happened? If so, how do you think Grandma and Uncle Frederick will react?
9. If you could talk to Uncle Frederick and Grandma, what would you say to them?
10. Can you think of another title for the story?
11. Uncle Frederick plays a small but important role in this story. Talk about it.

THE WHALES' SONG
Dyan Sheldon and Gary Blythe

12. Do you have a grandparent or older relation that tells you stories? Talk about it.

The Great Blue Whale

Kerry Hardie

Nobody knows
where he goes
nor what he does in the deep.

Nor why he sings
like a bird without wings,
nor where he eats and sleeps.

The blue whale roves
through watery groves,
his heart is the size of a car,

His tongue, on the scale,
makes zoologists pale –
it's as heavy as elephants are.

A blue whale's vein
without stress or strain
could be swum down by you or me.

He's the biggest feature
that ever did creature
the sky, the land or the sea.

The Whales' Hymn

Brian Patten

In an ocean before cold dawn broke
Covered by an overcoat
I lay awake in a boat
And heard a whale.

Hearing a song so solemn and so calm
It seemed absurd to feel alarm —
But I had a notion it sang
God's favourite hymn,

And spoke direct to Him.

Whales

1. Do you know the names of any kinds of whale? Skim through this unit and find the names of four kinds of whale.
2. The unit is divided into different parts. Each part has a heading. Under what heading would you find out about
   a.) how whales communicate
   b.) dangers to whales?

Whales are huge animals that live in the deep seas of our planet. Whales have flippers at the front of their bodies, fins on their backs and big strong tails. They also have a thick layer of fat that lies beneath their skin. This fat is called blubber and it keeps them warm.

Breathing

Whales spend most of their time underwater, but they need air to breathe. Every now and then they swim to the surface of the ocean to take a deep breath. A whale breathes air in through a blowhole on the top of its head. When the whale breathes air out, it sprays water out of its blowhole. This is called a spout.

Eating

Some whales have teeth and some whales don't. Whales without teeth are called baleen whales. They have baleen plates at the sides of their mouths. When a whale takes a huge gulp of water, these plates trap tiny plants and animals in a hairy fringe. Toothed whales have pointed teeth to help them catch fish, squid and sometimes even other whales.

Moving around

Many whales live in groups called pods. Adult whales make a circle around smaller baby whales to protect them from harm. If a whale is sick, the other whales help guide the sick whale to the surface of the sea for air. Whales spend the summer in cold seas where there is plenty of food. They travel up to 8,000 kilometres to get to warm waters where they have their families.

Sending messages

Whales can talk to each other underwater. They make strange noises that can travel for long distances. They have a special sense known as 'echo-location'. They make clicking noises that bounce like an echo off an object. This tells them where the object is and what size it is. Echo-location also helps them to find food. Some whales say 'hello' by touching each other with their flippers and by rubbing their heads together. The call of the blue whale can be heard from 1,000 kilometres away.

Different kinds of whale

The **blue whale** is the largest creature in the world. Some blue whales grow to 30 metres long. That's the same length as an aeroplane and bigger than the largest dinosaur! The blue whale can blow the highest spray from its spout, as high as nine metres or as tall as a house. Even a baby blue whale is enormous. It measures seven metres in length. It is bigger than any other mammal baby. It weighs more than 30 people together and drinks up to 500 litres of milk a day.

The blue whale

The **sperm whale** dives to the deepest parts of the sea and swims along the sea floor to collect food. It catches squid, lobsters and even sharks. But it is not a fussy eater. Its big mouth sweeps up all the rubbish that gathers on the seabed.

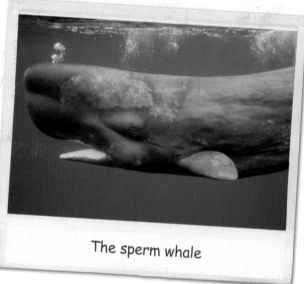

The sperm whale

The **killer whale** has beautiful black and white markings and shiny skin. It is a speedy swimmer and a fierce hunter. It eats fish, penguins, seals and sharks. It may even attack other whales. The killer whale is also a good acrobat and often leaps and twists out of the ocean or skims along the top of the water.

The killer whale

The white beluga whale

The humpback whale

The small **white beluga** whale is known as a friendly animal. Beluga whales travel in groups and like to chirp and call to their friends as they swim. Sailors called the beluga whale the 'sea canary' because of the whistling and squeaking noises it makes.

The **humpback** is the most playful whale. It loves to jump out of the ocean and splash the water with its tail and flippers. It is also very curious and likes to swim about on the surface of the ocean to see what's going on. A male humpback can make notes and sounds in patterns. These patterns can last up to half an hour.

Whale-hunting

People hunt the whale because many parts of its body can be used by humans. Long ago, whale bones were used for jewellery and for the handles of hairbrushes and toothbrushes. Blubber was used for making candles, face cream and lipstick.

About 80 years ago, whales had been hunted so much that they had almost disappeared. Rubbish and oil had also polluted the sea and the whales' home was in danger. People became very worried that these amazing creatures might become extinct. Finally, laws were passed to protect the whales. Now there are certain parts of the sea where they can live in peace and safety. However, some countries still believe in their right to hunt these animals.

Find out more at: www.greenpeace.org

The Song of the Whale

Kit Wright

Heaving mountain in the sea,
Whale, I heard you
Grieving.

Great Whale, crying for your life,
Crying for your kind, I knew
How we would use
Your dying.

Lipstick for our painted faces,
Polish for our shoes.

Tumbling mountain in the sea,
Whale, I heard you
Calling.

Bird-high notes, keening
Soaring:
At their edge a tiny drum
Like a heartbeat.

We would make you
Dumb.

In the forest of the sea,
Whale, I heard you
Singing,

Singing to your kind.
We'll never let you be.
Instead of life we choose

Lipstick for our painted faces,
Polish for our shoes.

1. Look at the *Whale-hunting* section on page 35 and this poem. How are they alike? How are they different?
2. Which piece do you prefer? Why?
3. Fold a sheet of paper in two. On one side, write down reasons why you might hunt whales. On the other side, write down reasons against whale-hunting.
4. Make a list of 'whale words' that you have read.

Tiger Lily: A Heroine in the Making

Maeve Friel

This is me (and my dog Rosie!). I live with my mum, Vicky, in One-End Street in The Middle of Nowhere, a hilly village where NOTHING EVER HAPPENS. Everything is shut up or falling to pieces and everyone is either getting old or not old enough or moving away or just plain weird.

It's not a promising place for a heroine but that is EXACTLY what I have decided to be. I am going to become a Knight Errant and roam the world in search of adventure...
Now what is the best way to get out of here?

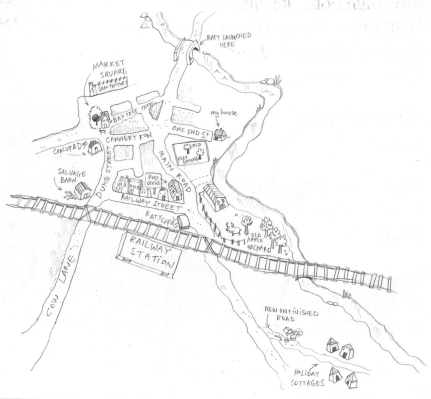

'Lily! Lily! For the last time! LILY!' Mum roared from the bottom of the stairs.

Lily did not hear her mother shouting. That was because only her mother called her Lily *Lily*: everyone else called her Tiger. But the main reason she didn't hear anything was because she had her nose stuck in a book.

All her life Tiger Lily had been mad about books. Her house on One-End

Street was STUFFED with them. As well as the books on the bookshelves, there were books in the bedrooms, books in the hall, books in the bathroom, books in the kitchen and books on the stairs. There were books on tables and under tables, books on chairs and between chairs and behind chairs. There were even books under the stairs along with the Christmas decorations and an inflatable giraffe. The whole house was suffering from a bad case of BOOK CREEP. Books were taking over every single empty space. And where there were no books, there were poems. Tiger Lily sellotaped them to doors and walls. She even stuck a bit of her favourite poem, *The Pied Piper of Hamelin*, on the fridge under two magnets.

'So munch on, crunch on,
Take your nuncheon,
Breakfast, supper,
Dinner, luncheon!'

Tiger Lily's mother, Vicky, loved books too. She drove the mobile library van and sometimes took Lily with her when she went on her rounds of all the little villages in their valley. Everywhere they went, there were people with their noses stuck in books. The library van regulars liked romances and detective stories. The hill walkers carried slim volumes of poetry in their rucksacks. The summer visitors snoozed on the beach with thick paperbacks rising and falling on their tummies.

But Tiger was more than just fond of reading: she was OBSESSED!

She had read how Fern had rescued the little pig Wilbur from her father's axe in *Charlotte's Web*.

She was green with envy that Alice had followed the White Rabbit down the rabbit-hole and found herself in Wonderland.

Sometimes, she wished that she could have a monkey like Pippi Longstocking, and live alone in a cottage where she could do exactly what she wanted when she wanted.

At other times, she longed to find a mysterious cousin in the attic like the girl in *The Secret Garden*.

But best of all, she wished that she could be like Jo March in *Little Women*, and sell her beautiful chestnut hair (if only she had beautiful chestnut hair) to save her family from certain ruin. (Which was what was going to happen if her mum didn't pass her driving test for the big new-style library vans.)

All this reading had gone to Tiger's head. It was always giving her ingenious ideas, and it had got her into trouble *countless* times before – like the time when she had dug up the garden looking for jewels after reading *The Treasure Seekers*. But she had forgotten all that when, on the first Saturday of the half-term holiday, she made up her mind that she too would be a HEROINE.

But which sort of heroine could she be? What was the best way to go about it?

How to be a Heroine

Redress a wrong

Topple a tyrant

Track down a criminal

Solve a mystery

Win a war

~~Marry a hero?~~

She turned over a new leaf in her notebook and drew up a list.

Any of these would do except for the last one. She wanted to be a heroine in her own right, not a wishy-washy princess, and anyway she didn't intend to marry anyone for a very long time. She scratched out the last entry and looked at the list again.

There was still a problem. Since absolutely nothing ever happened in The Middle of Nowhere, she would have to go a-roaming in search of adventure. But how could she go a-roaming when she didn't have a horse? Or a hot-air balloon or a broomstick, a carriage or a man-o'-war[1]? She didn't even have a bicycle.

And there was another problem.

★ What do you think might happen to Tiger Lily and her mum?

★ Think of other ways to become a hero/heroine. Add to Tiger Lily's list.

[1] A 'man **of** war' was a powerful warship with sails and cannons.

Every heroine needs a companion – a squire or a wise fairy or devoted slave; a family of younger brothers and sisters might have done except that she didn't have any...

There wasn't even anybody her age in the village now that her best friend Sammy had moved to the city. There was only Milo Hannibal and his gang and the little wieners[2] at the Mothers and Toddlers' Group.

She was lying on her bed, wondering where on earth she could find a TRUSTY DEVOTED companion, the kind that would stop at nothing, who would even lay down their life for her if the need arose, when....

'LILY!'

Tiger Lily was so shocked by the sudden appearance of her mother looming over her in a bright red puffa jacket that she jumped off the bed, upset a pile of books and accidentally stood on Rosie, who started barking unhelpfully.

(Rosie was a nervous and very skinny three-legged greyhound that Lily had rescued from under the railway bridge a few days earlier.)

'Lily, didn't you hear me shouting? We're really late. We've got to go NOW! I've got a driving lesson and then a meeting with my Awful Boss and after that I'm going to Auntie Pamela's to get my hair done. Come on! Hurry Up!'

As usual, Tiger Lily thought that her mum was far too bright. Her clothes were too colourful – canary yellow boots! Flowery skirt! Spearmint leggings! – and she had far, far too much frizzy hair that fell around her shoulders in hundreds of little corkscrews.

Personally, Lily would have preferred a quieter, duller mum – one like Marmee in *Little Women*, instead of The Red Queen from *Alice*. ☆

'Do you know,' she mused, holding Rosie's jaws clamped shut with both hands to stop the yowling, 'there are hardly any mums in books. Pippi Longstocking

☆ Can you think of a 'Mum' character in a book you have read?

[2] Little guys.

41

doesn't have a mum and neither does Alice; and Mary Lennox, the girl from *The Secret Garden*, was an orphan and so was that girl who went up the Amazon with her governess...'

Mum burst out laughing. 'So you'd like to get rid of me too, is that what you're saying? Honestly, Lily!'

She dropped a quick kiss on the top of Lily's head. 'If you hurry up, I'll take you round to Granny's. Or do you want to stay with Auntie Pamela at Curl Up & Dye?'

But Tiger Lily wasn't listening. She was steering her canoe through river channels choked with mangrove roots, heading for a magical opera house in the middle of the Amazonian rainforest.

'LILY! You're miles away. Stop day-dreaming. We have to go NOW!'

And her mum set off across the living room, skilfully slaloming around the piles of books on the floor. 'By the way,' she shouted over her shoulder, 'we need to talk about that dog. You must find a home for it before you go back to school.'

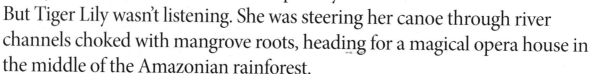

1. What job did Tiger Lily's mother have?
2. What did Tiger Lily call the village where she lived? Why?
3. Why did Tiger Lily cross out 'Marry a Hero' from her list?

4. What words and phrases does the author use to build up a picture of Tiger Lily's mum?
5. Scan the story to find the titles of books Tiger Lily has read. Have you read any of them? Talk about them.
6. Can you picture what Tiger Lily's home looks like? What words or phrases from the story help you?
7. Make a list of words from the story that are new to you. How could you figure out what they mean?

8. What kind of character is Tiger Lily's mother, do you think?
9. Did anything in the story surprise you?
10. What does Tiger Lily think of princesses in story books? Do you agree with her?

11. If you could be a character from a book, who would it be? Why would you like to be that character?

Irish musical instruments

1. Scan the headings in these two pages:
    a.) Have you ever heard one of these instruments being played?
    b.) Can you play any of them?

The harp

The harp has been played in Ireland for many hundreds of years. The oldest harp in Ireland today is the Brian Boru harp. It is about 600 years old. It is made from oak and willow with brass strings. The Brian Boru harp is kept in Trinity College in Dublin. Long ago in Ireland, harpists were very important people. Harpists played their music in the homes and castles of Irish chieftains.

The most famous harpist was Turlough O'Carolan, who lived about 300 years ago. Although he was blind, he travelled the country playing his harp.

The uilleann pipes

The uilleann pipes are like Scottish bagpipes, but the bag is filled with air using a bellows. The bellows is held under the elbow.
The Irish word for elbow is *uilleann*.
The uilleann pipes are often used to play a lament when someone has died.

The bodhrán

The bodhrán is a kind of drum. It is made of goatskin that has been stretched over a round wooden frame. The bodhrán is played with the hand or a stick.

The tin whistle

For many people in Ireland the tin whistle is the first musical instrument that they learn to play. It is cheap to buy and is fairly easy to play.

Whistles have been played around the world for many hundreds of years. Some were made from bamboo and others were made from reeds. Some were even made from hollowed-out bones. Bone whistles have been found in Dublin. They are about 800 years old.

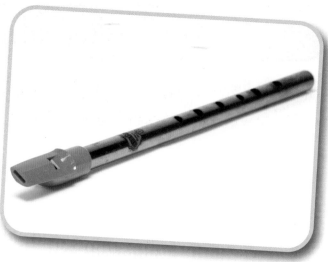

The fiddle

The fiddle is one of the most popular Irish musical instruments. There are hundreds of fiddle players in Ireland today. A fiddle is made of about 80 different pieces of wood. A special glue is used to hold the pieces together. No nails or screws are used.

1. What Irish instrument is a kind of drum?
2. Why is the tin whistle the first musical instrument that many people learn to play?
3. Which instrument would you like to play? Talk about it.
4. Name some other musical instruments.

Let's make music

You can make your own musical instruments using very simple things. Why not try this experiment at home or in school?

Music in bottles

You will need:
- Five bottles of the same shape and size
- Some water
- A few drops of ink or food colouring

1. Fill the first bottle with water almost to the top.

2. Fill the second bottle about three-quarters full, the third bottle half full and the fourth a quarter full. Leave the fifth bottle empty.

3. Add ink or food colouring to the water in each bottle to make it easier to see.

4. Blow across the top of each bottle.

What did you notice?
A different note came from each bottle because there was a different amount of air in each. The bottle with the small amount of air made a high note. The bottle with the large amount of air made a low note.

- Practise blowing into the bottles. Can you make up a tune?

- Now try doing the experiment using different shaped bottles and different levels of water. How many notes can you make?

Greedy Dog

James Hurley

This dog will eat anything.

Apple cores and bacon fat,
Milk you poured out for the cat.
He likes the string that ties the roast
And relishes hot buttered toast.
Hide your chocolates! He's a thief,
He'll even eat your handkerchief.
And if you don't like sudden shocks,
Carefully conceal your socks.
Leave some soup without the lid
And you'll wish you never did.
When you think he must be full,
You find him gobbling bits of wool,
Orange peel or paper bags,
Dusters and old cleaning rags.

This dog will eat anything,
Except for mushrooms and cucumber.

Now what is wrong with those, I wonder.

The Giggler Treatment

Roddy Doyle

CHAPTER EIGHT

WHICH SHOULD PROBABLY BE CALLED

CHAPTER...

HANG ON.
ONE, TWO, THREE, FOUR...
OH, STOP MESSING AND
GET ON WITH THE STORY

The day before Mister Mack's foot headed straight for the poo, just before it got too dark to play outside, the Mack brothers, Jimmy and Robbie, broke the kitchen window.

They were playing football with a burst ball when it happened. Robbie Mack gave the ball a whack with his big toe. It bounced off Jimmy Mack's head, flew at the window, and cracked the glass.

'Ouch!' said Robbie. 'Me toe!'

'Ouch!' said Jimmy. 'Me head!'

'Wah!' said Mister Mack. 'Me window!'

He was upstairs when he heard the noise. He was in the bathroom, putting a plaster on his finger. He'd cut his finger putting new glass into the kitchen window, just five minutes before the ball cracked it.

He ran downstairs into the kitchen and saw the broken window. So he kept running, out into the garden. 'Who did that?' he shouted.

'Not us,' said Robbie. 'The ball did it.'

'I only just fixed it,' said Mister Mack.

'It's not fair.' Mister Mack had had a very hard day.

'That's seven times I've had to fix that window,' he said, 'in seven days!' He looked at Robbie and Jimmy.

'Boys, boys, boys,' he said. 'How many times am I going to have to fix it?'

'Eight,' said Robbie.

Robbie wasn't being smart or cheeky when he said that. He was giving Mister Mack the correct answer. The window had been broken seven times, and now he was going to have to fix it once more. Seven and one made eight. So Robbie was right. But poor Mister Mack had had a very hard day. He had spent all day testing cream crackers, and they were very boring biscuits. In fact, Mister Mack didn't think that they were really biscuits at all. They were always perfectly, boringly square and they tasted like nothing except what they were, boring old cream crackers. And poor Mister Mack had been measuring and eating them all day. He was stuffed to the tonsils with cream crackers. He knew he'd dream about cream crackers tonight. He always had the same cream cracker dream after a day of measuring

Do you think the story so far is funny? Which parts?

48

and eating cream crackers. It wasn't a dream about killer ninja cream crackers or beautiful, brown-eyed cream crackers or anything interesting like that. No chance. In this dream, Mister Mack was always surrounded by talking cream crackers, hundreds of them, all saying the most boring things ever.

'Babies are smaller than adults. Isn't that interesting?'

'Toilet paper is usually white but not always. Isn't that interesting?'

'A car has four wheels but a bike has only two. Isn't that interesting?'

All night the talking cream crackers would be yapping at him. (That was another reason why Mister Mack loved fig-rolls. They never talked when he went to sleep.) He wasn't looking forward to bedtime, even though he was very tired. He could already hear the cream crackers mumbling away in his brain.

'Some pyjamas have stripes and some don't have any stripes at all. Isn't that interesting?'

But that wasn't the worst part of the day. Something strange had happened to Mister Mack at lunchtime. A vulture had swooped down from a tree and robbed his sandwiches. And, before he'd had time to get over the shock, the vulture came back and robbed his flask. Then he'd had to fix the broken kitchen window for the seventh time in seven days, and he'd cut his finger doing it. He was hungry and tired and his finger was sore and the cream crackers were already yapping at him.

'If you put your feet in water, they get wet. Isn't that interesting?'

The vulture had stuck his tongue out at him as he flew away with the flask. The flask had been full of chicken soup, Mister Mack's all-time favourite.

☆ How do you know Mister Mack did not enjoy his job?

☆ Can you think of other 'interesting' things the cream crackers might say to Mister Mack?

49

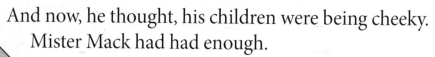

And now, he thought, his children were being cheeky. Mister Mack had had enough.

'Go up to your room,' he told Robbie and Jimmy.

'But I'm hungry,' said Jimmy.

'I don't care,' said Mister Mack. 'Go up to your room.'

And that was why, the next morning, the poo was waiting for Mister Mack. What Mister Mack didn't know – and what nobody else knew – was that the Gigglers were listening to him. They were in the cupboard under the stairs.

They looked at one another and nodded.

'The Treatment?' said the smallest, very quietly.

'The Treatment,' said the biggest.

'Poo?' said the smallest.

'Poo,' said the biggest.

---

1. What did Mr Mack think of cream crackers?
2. What strange thing happened to Mister Mack at lunchtime?

3. Mr Mack didn't have a good day. List, in order, what happened to him during the day.
4. Some of the things that happen in this extract are very far-fetched. Other things are quite normal. Give two examples of each.

5. What, do you think, did the Gigglers mean by 'The Treatment'?
6. Does Mister Mack get on well with his sons? Talk about it.
7. Do you think Mister Mack should get a different job? Why?
8. Can you think of another title for this chapter?

9. What treat do you like to have for your lunch?
10. Do you ever have unusual dreams? You might like to talk about them.
11. What is the most boring job you can imagine?

Roddy Doyle

THE Giggler TREATMENT

Roger the Dog

Ted Hughes

Asleep he wheezes at his ease.
He only wakes to scratch his fleas.

He hogs the fire, he bakes his head
As if it were a loaf of bread.

He's just a sack of snoring dog.
You can lug him like a log.

You can roll him with your foot,
He'll stay snoring where he's put.

I take him out for exercise,
He rolls in cowclap up to his eyes.

He will not race, he will not romp,
He saves his strength for gobble and chomp.

He'll work as hard as you could wish
Emptying his dinner dish.

Then flops flat, and digs down deep,
Like a miner, into sleep.

Safety first!

1. Look at the diagram of the bicycle. Can you name each numbered part?
2. What road signs do you pass on your way to school? Talk about them.

Many children travel to and from school on a bicycle. Cycling is a very good kind of exercise and it is great fun. But if you use a bicycle you should remember that roads can be very dangerous. It is easy to have an accident if you do not cycle carefully.

To be safe on a bicycle you should always:
- Wear a helmet.
- Wear bright clothes and reflective strips at night so that you can be seen more easily.
- Use lights when cycling in the dark. The front light must be white (or green) and the back light must be red.
- Obey the traffic lights! They are not just for motorists.
- Cycle on the road – not on the footpath.
- Cycle one behind the other – if two or more are cycling together. Never cycle side by side.

Taking care of your bicycle

By taking care of your bicycle you will make sure that it is safe to ride and that it runs smoothly. Good brakes are most important. From time to time check that the brake pads haven't worn down. The chain should be kept cleaned and oiled. Check that the bell is working. Make sure the tyres are not flat or worn thin. Old worn tyres will skid easily in the rain.

What to wear

You should always wear a helmet when you are cycling. It could save your life by protecting your head if you fall from your bicycle. Make sure that it fits properly; it should not be loose. Don't forget to fasten the chin-strap. A good helmet is very light and has air-holes to keep you cool.

Clothing must keep a cyclist warm and dry without being too hot. Bright clothes are easily seen by motorists especially at night. Reflective armbands and reflective strips will make it even easier for motorists to see you.

Find out more about safe cycling on the Road Safety Association website: www.rsa.ie

1. Do you know any other road signs?
2. What do you think are the most important ways to stay safe when you cycle?
3. Make a chart of the different ways that the children in your class come to school.

Oh, Woe Ith Me!

Bruce Lansky

Ath I wath biking
down the thtweet,
I hit a bump
and lotht my theat.

I cwathed my bike
into a twee.
I thcwathed my fathe—
oh, woe ith me.

My bike ith wecked.
I've no excuthe.
And wortht of all,
my tooth ith looth.

1. Read the title of the story and the introduction. What might the story be about?
2. Look at the pictures. Can you predict more now?

The Pain and the Great One: Soupy Saturdays

Judy Blume

Jake (the Pain) and Abigail (the Great One) are brother and sister. Like most brothers and sisters they fight and argue about almost everything. In this extract, they go with their parents to visit Aunt Diana and her husband Mitchell.

Then Mom called, 'Who wants to go for a bike ride?'
'I do,' Dad answered.
'Me too,' the Pain sang. 'Come on, Abigail – let's go!'
'No, thank you,' I said, 'I'm going to stay here and play with the baby.'
The Pain gave me a look.
When the three of them were gone, Mitchell said, 'Hey, Abigail...'
Mitchell hardly ever says anything. When he does, he talks very softly. You have to listen carefully or you'll miss what he's saying. 'There's no traffic on our road,' he told me. 'It's a good place to learn to ride a bike.'
I pretended I didn't hear him.
'Abigail...' he said, louder. Then he repeated what he'd just said – about how their road is a good place to learn to ride a bike.
'No, thank you,' I told him. 'I'm playing with the baby.'
'Actually,' Aunt Diana said, 'the baby is ready for his nap.' She scooped up Jackson and carried him away.
I could feel Mitchell looking at me.
'I'll just sit here and read,' I told him. 'I brought a book.'
'You know, I'm a pretty good teacher,' Mitchell said. 'I teach seventh- and eighth-grade maths.'
'What does maths have to do with riding a bike?' I asked.

Why do you think Abigail pretended not to hear?

55

'Well... some kids think they can't learn maths,' Mitchell said, 'so they're afraid to try.'

'I'm good at maths,' I told him.

I'm good at other things too, I thought. *I can blade better than anyone I know. I can jump rope, turn an almost-perfect cartwheel and make pancakes with hardly any help. The Pain is hopeless at those things. So how come he can ride a bike? It's so unfair.*

'All it takes to ride a bike is practice,' Mitchell said.

'Practise *falling*?' I said. 'No, thank you.'

Mitchell opened a bag. He pulled out padded pants and a padded shirt. He pulled out knee pads, elbow pads, wrist guards, padded gloves and a helmet with a face guard. He stuck the helmet on my head.

'Where'd you get all this stuff?' I asked.

'I collect it,' Mitchell said. 'Just in case.'

'Just in case *what*?' But I was thinking, *Hmm... maybe with all this padding I should try...* Then I thought, *No I have tried...* Then I thought, *Yes, but if I don't try one more time, I'll never know. And this will positively, absolutely be my final try...*

So when Mitchell held out the shirt, I took it and pulled it on. It was way too big. So was everything else. But Mitchell didn't care. Soon I was padded everywhere. I was so padded I waddled like a penguin.

Mitchell led me to the front door. I caught a glimpse of myself in the hall mirror. *No one would recognize me in all this stuff*, I thought. *No one would know it's me, Abigail Carly Porter, from 10 Larken Road.*

'Riding a bike is like learning to swim,' Mitchell told me. 'Once you learn you'll never forget.'

'I'm good at swimming,' I said. Then I added, 'Not like my brother, who's afraid to put his face in the water.'

'You'll be good at bike riding too.' I shook my head. Mitchell patted my back. 'You'll see,' he said.

I reminded him to make sure the seat on my bike was very low. I reminded him that I needed to be able to put my feet on the ground whenever I wanted. Mitchell held the bike steady as I got on. My knees were shaking. My stomach felt funny.

'Now... close your eyes,' Mitchell said.

'Close my eyes!' I said. 'Are you crazy?'

'Come on, Abigail. Just close your eyes and *feel* yourself balance on the bike.'

'I can't!' I cried. 'I can't!'

'Yes, you can,' Mitchell said.

'Promise you won't let go?'

'I promise.'

So I closed my eyes. *Maybe I'll never open them*, I thought.

'OK,' Mitchell said. 'Very good. Now let's give it a try.'

His voice was so soft I wasn't sure what he said. So I didn't move. I just sat on the bike with my eyes closed.

'Abigail,' Mitchell said, 'Open your eyes and pedal.'

'Pedal?' I said, as if that was a crazy idea.

'Yes, pedal.'

So I started to pedal. I pedalled very, very slowly.

'Faster,' Mitchell called. 'Pedal faster.'

So I did.

'That's it... Keep pedalling.'

Mitchell ran, holding on to the back of my bike. As long as he was running with me and holding on to the bike, I was OK. The second he let go, I fell.

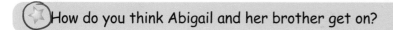

How do you think Abigail and her brother get on?

I was glad I was wearing padded *everything*. 'You see!' I told Mitchell. 'I knew I would fall.'

'You know why you fell?' Mitchell asked. 'You fell because you stopped pedalling.'

'I always fall when I stop,' I told him.

'*Aha*!' Mitchell said.

'Aha what?'

'*Stop* equals *fall*,' Mitchell said. 'We've solved the problem.'

'What problem?'

'Your problem,' Mitchell said, as if he was talking about maths. 'If you want to stop pedalling, you have to brake and step to the ground. Pedal, brake, step to the ground. Got that?'

'Pedal, brake, step to the ground,' I repeated.

'That's it,' Mitchell said. 'Let's try again.' ✩

So I tried again. Mitch held my bike steady until I got going. Then he ran with the bike. I couldn't tell when he let go. I just kept pedalling and pedalling – until I braked – and jumped off my bike. This time I didn't fall. But my bike did. It fell over on its side. Too bad it wasn't padded like me.

'You know why your bike fell?' Mitch called, running to catch up with me. I shook my head.

'Because you let go,' he said. 'When you step off your bike you have to hold onto it.'

'You didn't tell me that,' I said. 'You said, "Pedal, brake, step to the ground."'

✩ Would you have tried again?

'Well, now you know,' Mitch said, very softly. 'So, let's give it another try.'

'Do I have to?'

'If you want to be able to ride, you do.'

I thought about Emily, Sasha and Kaylee on their bikes. Then I thought about the Pain singing, *Abigail can't ride a bike...* and how good it would feel to prove he was wrong.

So I tried again.

And again.

And again.

Soon I was pedalling on my own. And instead of running after me, Mitch was pumping his arm. Yes! I reminded myself to hold on to my bike every time I came to a stop. *Pedal, brake, step to the ground... Pedal, brake, step to the ground.* By the time Mom, Dad and the Pain came back, I was riding up and down the road. I was even practising wobbly turns. I couldn't wait to tell my friends!

Then I heard the Pain call, 'Who's that weirdo on wheels?'

'That's no weirdo,' Mitch called back. 'That's your sister.'

'My sister can't ride a bike,' the Pain called.

I whizzed by the Pain, signing, 'Oh yes, I can!' Then I tried a showy-offy turn, lost my balance, and flew off my bike – right into a big pile of leaves.

☆ What does this tell you about Abigail?

After a minute I picked myself up. 'How about that trick?' I called. 'I'll bet you can't do a flying leap like that!'

The Pain shook his head. 'This proves it. You *are* a weirdo on wheels!'

'That's why you're glad I'm your sister,' I told him.

'Who says I'm glad?'

'Think about it,' I said. 'You could have a boring, ordinary sister. Instead, you have me!'

Then I got back on my bike and rode away, with the Pain calling, 'Abigail... wait! Abigail...' But I was already pedalling as fast as I could. And inside my helmet, I was smiling.

1. What job did Mitchell have?
2. Why did Mitchell ask Abigail to close her eyes when she first got on the bike?
3. What did Mitchell say riding a bike was like?

4. How do you know Mitchell was delighted when Abigail started to pedal on her own?
5. Was Mitchell a good teacher? Find examples that show this.
6. Abigail's mood changes during the story. Find some examples.

7. What country do you think this story is set in? Why do you think this?
8. Describe how you think Abigail felt when she sat on the bike for the first time.
9. How do you think the Pain feels now that Abigail can cycle?

10. Do you know how to cycle? If you do, tell the class how you learned.
11. Have you ever found something difficult to learn? Did you stick with it or did you give up? How did you feel?

TV guide

1. What television programmes do you like to watch? Talk about them.

TV guide

Volume 10   Issue 6

guide

Your guide to TV and radio for the week

Forever
The interview!

Running Away to the Circus
Mr Pepper talks about life on the road

Space Mad
A season of classic science-fiction movies

The Saturday Show
Michelle Moore talks about ten years of hosting The Saturday Show

Evening Television for Saturday, 30 May • • • • • • • •

Channel One

5:00 **Nature Trail**
Documentary on the hedgehog.

6:00 **News**
Including sports results and the
weather forecast.

6:50 **Question Time**
Topic: Computer games today
Interviews with children about
their favourite games.

7:50 **Game Show**
Jack Ryan and Gloria Byrne
host a fantastic show with three
surprise celebrity guests.

8:30 **History Hour**
This week's history hour
takes a look at the Egyptians.

9:30 **The Saturday Show**
Michelle Moore interviews
two famous female soccer
players of the 21st Century.
Musical performance by the
new Irish band *Forever*.
Comedian Ronnie Devine
rounds up the show with
a great stand-up act.

Channel Two

5:00 **Cartoon Time**
A half-hour of hilarious cartoons.

5:30 **The Greatest Show in the World**
Featuring Mr Pepper's Amazing
Acrobats.

6:00 **Space Documentary**
Featuring exclusive interviews
with astronauts.

7:00 **Riddles and Rhymes**
Tune in this week for your
favourite riddles and rhymes.

8:00 **Galaxy Battle**
A classic science-fiction film
about astronauts.

10:00 **News**
Including sports results and the
weather forecast.

1. What programmes would you watch if you wanted to find out about
   a.) space   b.) soccer
   c.) Egyptians   d.) weather?
2. Which programme would you most like to
   a.) watch b.) take part in?
3. Create your own TV guide for Channel Three.
4. In groups act out a TV show of your choice.

1. Look closely at the artwork. How many creatures can you name?
2. How many seasons can you spot?
3. What do you think might happen in the story?

THE WINTER HEDGEHOG

Ann and Reg Cartwright

One cold, misty autumn afternoon, the hedgehogs gathered in a wood. They were searching the undergrowth for leaves for their nests, preparing for the long sleep of winter.

All, that is, except one.

The smallest hedgehog had overheard two foxes talking about winter.

'What is winter?' he had asked his mother.

'Winter comes when we are asleep,' she replied. 'It can be beautiful, but it can also be dangerous, cruel and very, very cold. It's not for the likes of us. Now go to sleep.'

But the smallest hedgehog couldn't sleep.

As evening fell he slipped away to look for winter. When hedgehogs are determined they can move very swiftly, and soon the little hedgehog was far from home. An owl swooped down from high in a tree. 'Hurry home,' he called. 'It's time for your long sleep.' But on and on went the smallest hedgehog until the sky turned dark and the trees were nothing but shadows.

The next morning, the hedgehog awoke to find the countryside covered in fog.

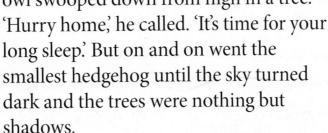

Do you think the smallest hedgehog should listen to his mother? Why?

'Who goes there?' called a voice, and a large rabbit emerged from the mist, amazed to see a hedgehog about with winter coming on.

'I'm looking for winter,' replied the hedgehog. 'Can you tell me where it is?'

'Hurry home,' said the rabbit. 'Winter is on its way and it's no time for hedgehogs.'

But the smallest hedgehog wouldn't listen. He was determined to find winter.

Days passed. The little hedgehog found plenty of slugs and insects to eat, but he couldn't find winter anywhere.

Then one day the air turned icy cold. Birds flew home to their roosts and the animals hid in their burrows and warrens. The smallest hedgehog felt very lonely and afraid and wished he was asleep with the other hedgehogs. But it was too late to turn back now!

That night winter came. A frosty wind swept through the grass and blew the last straggling leaves from the trees. In the morning the whole countryside was covered in a carpet of snow.

'Winter!' cried the smallest hedgehog. 'I've found it at last.' And all the birds flew down from the trees to join him.

The trees were completely bare and the snow sparkled on the grass. The little hedgehog went to the river to drink, but it was frozen. He shivered, shook his prickles and stepped on to the ice. His feet began to slide and the faster he scurried, the faster he sped across it. 'Winter is wonderful,' he cried. At first he did not see the fox, like a dark shadow, slinking towards him.

'Hello! Come and join me,' he called as the fox reached the riverbank. But the fox only heard the rumble of his empty belly.

What words does the writer use to describe the coming of winter?

With one leap he pounced on to the ice.

When the little hedgehog saw his sly yellow eyes he understood what the fox was about.

But every time he tried to run away he slipped on the ice. He curled into a ball and spiked his prickles.

'Ouch!' cried the fox. The sharp prickles stabbed his paws and he reeled towards the centre of the river where he disappeared beneath the thin ice.

'That was close,' the smallest hedgehog cried to himself. 'Winter is beautiful, but it is also cruel, dangerous and very, very cold.'

Winter was everywhere: in the air, in the trees, on the ground and in the hedgerows. Colder and colder it grew until the snow froze under the hedgehog's feet. Then the snow came again and a cruel north wind picked it up and whipped it into a blizzard. The night fell as black as ink and he lost his way.

'Winter is dangerous and cruel and very, very cold,' moaned the little hedgehog.

Luck saved him. A hare scurrying home gave him shelter in his burrow. By morning the snow was still falling, but gently now, covering everything it touched in a soft white blanket. The smallest hedgehog was enchanted as he watched the pattern his paws made. Reaching the top of a hill, he rolled into a ball and spun over and over, turning himself into a great white snowball as he went. Down and down he rolled until he reached the feet of two children building a snowman.

'Hey, look at this,' said the little girl, 'a perfect head for our snowman.'

'I'm a hedgehog,' he cried. But no one heard his tiny hedgehog voice.

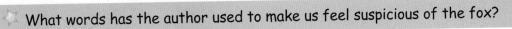

What words has the author used to make us feel suspicious of the fox?

Can you spot the hedgehog in the picture? Look closely!

65

The girl placed the hedgehog snowball on the snowman's body and the boy used a carrot for a nose and pebbles for the eyes. 'Let me out,' shouted the hedgehog. But the children just stood back and admired their work before going home for lunch.

When the children had gone, the cold and hungry hedgehog nibbled at the carrot nose. As he munched, the sun came out and the snow began to melt. He blinked in the bright sunlight, tumbled down the snowman's body and was free.

Time went on. The hedgehog saw the world in its winter cloak. He saw bright red berries disappear from the hedgerows as the birds collected them for their winter larders. And he watched children speed down the hill on their sleighs.

The winter passed. One day the air grew warmer and the river began to flow again. A stoat, who had changed his coat to winter white, changed it back to brown. Then the little hedgehog found crocuses and snowdrops beneath the trees and he knew it was time to go home. Slowly he made his way back to the wood.

From out of every log, sleepy hedgehogs were emerging from their long sleep.

'Where have you been?' they called to the smallest hedgehog.

'I found winter,' he replied.

'And what was it like?' asked his mother.

'It was wonderful and beautiful, but it was also...'

'Dangerous, cruel and very, very cold,' finished his mother.

But she was answered by a yawn, a sigh and a snore and the smallest hedgehog was fast asleep.

1. How did the smallest hedgehog first hear of winter?
2. How did the hedgehog protect himself from the fox?

3. What food did the hedgehog find to eat?
4. What signs were there that winter had passed?
5. List these creatures in the order they appear in the story: fox, hare, owl, slugs, birds, rabbit, stoat.

6. 'Winter is beautiful, but it is also cruel.' Why did the hedgehog say this? Do you agree?
7. How do we know that the fox intended to eat the hedgehog?
8. How would you describe the hedgehog's character?
9. Can you think of another title for the story?
10. Tell the story from the fox's point of view.

11. What is your favourite season? Why?
12. Animals defend themselves in different ways. Talk about it.

THE WINTER HEDGEHOG
Ann & Reg Cartwright

RED FOX Mini Treasures

Hedgehogs

1. Talk about hedgehogs. The headings in the fact map will help you:
    a.) body and size   b.) food and sleep   c.) home
    d.) hibernation   e.) hedgehogs in danger   f.) where found

A fact map is a useful way to organise what you know. This is a fact map about hedgehogs.

Body and size		Food and sleep
Home		Hibernation
Hedgehogs in danger		Where found

Body and size

A hedgehog is a small animal, with sharp prickly spines. It has about 5000 spines altogether. These spines are very stiff and protect the hedgehog from other animals. As many as 500 fleas live amongst a hedgehog's spines. When the hedgehog is in danger, it curls up and sticks out its spines. The hedgehog sleeps curled up in a ball.

Type:	Mammal
Diet:	Carnivore
Size:	13 to 30cm long (30cm is about the length of your ruler)
Weight:	from about 400 grams to 1kg (a bag of sugar weighs 1kg)
Name:	Makes a pig-like grunt when hunting for food (hog = pig)
Irish name:	Gráinneog meaning 'horrible one'

Food and sleep

The hedgehog is a nocturnal creature. This means that it sleeps during the day and comes out at night. The hedgehog has a very strong sense of smell and good hearing, which it uses to find its way around as its eyesight is weak. When the hedgehog comes out at night it hunts for snails, worms, insects and frogs. The hedgehog can travel up to three kilometres at night searching for food.

Home and hibernation

A hedgehog's home is called a nest. It is made of dry leaves. A hedgehog's nest can be found in lots of places: in ditches, under bushes and near hedges. In late autumn, the weather gets colder and food becomes scarce, so the hedgehog prepares for its long winter sleep called 'hibernation'. To get ready, the hedgehog rolls around in dry dead leaves to make a thick warm blanket. Then it finds a dry sheltered spot away from danger.

The hedgehog's prickly spines

A desert hedgehog

Where hedgehogs are found

There are many different kinds of hedgehog. They are found in many parts of the world. There are hedgehogs in Ireland and other parts of Europe, Russia and China. Hedgehogs also live in the deserts of Africa and Asia. To escape from the hot sun and all kinds of dangers, desert hedgehogs dig burrows deep in the cool sand.

Be alert!

Watch out for hedgehogs on the streets and roads during the evening and at night. Many hedgehogs are killed by traffic when they are crossing the road in the dark. They can't run very fast and the lights of the cars dazzle them. Instead of running to safety they curl up into a tight ball. Another danger to hedgehogs is pools and ponds with steep banks. Hedgehogs can swim but can become trapped because they are not able to scramble up the sheer sides.

Watch out!
Hedgehog crossing the road

Food and sleep
- Nocturnal
- Strong sense of hearing and smell
- Curls up to sleep
- Eats snails, worms, insects and frogs

Body and size
- 5000 prickly spines
- 13-30cm
- 400g-1kg
- Curls up to avoid danger

Home
- Called a nest
- Made of dry leaves
- Found under bushes and in ditches and hedges

Where found

Hedgehogs in danger

Hibernation

1. Look at this partly completed fact map. What new things did you learn about the hedgehog? What notes would you put in the blank boxes?
2. Find out which other animals hibernate.
3. Choose one of these animals and make your own fact map about it.

70

What is Fog?

Anon

Puffs of dragon smoke
Curling round hedges and trees.

Clouds of steam from a giant's kettle
Pouring out over the city.

The breath from a dinosaur's nostrils
Blurring the world into a grey shadow.

The Wild Wind

Anon

Sweeping down the street,
Swerving through the trees,
Snatching leaves and twigs
To whisk in its breeze.

Whistling round the chimneys,
Whooshing under floors,
Sniffing at the windows,
Snapping shut the doors.

Shattering the silence
Wherever it goes,
Swirling, twirling, whirling,
The wild wind blows.

Weather

1. What games would you play
   a.) in dry weather b.) in wet weather?
2. Make a list of as many weather words as you can.

Forecasting the weather

People called meteorologists study the weather and prepare the weather forecast for TV and radio. They use information gathered from weather stations around the country and from satellites in space. Using a computer, the meteorologist can work out the next day's weather.

Weather satellite

Met Éireann Headquarters in Glasnevin, Dublin

In 1986, a group of 12 schoolchildren in China were sucked up by a tornado. The tornado carried them 20 kilometres and dropped them among sand dunes. All of the children escaped completely unhurt.

In 1939, a shower of frogs fell on the village of Trowbridge in England. Strong winds had gathered up the frogs from lakes and streams.

In 1940, a shower of silver coins fell in Russia. A tornado had uncovered a treasure chest. It carried the chest to a nearby village where the coins fell out.

The biggest hailstones ever fell on Bangladesh, near India, on 14th April, 1986. Each hailstone weighed over 1 kilogram and 92 people are said to have been killed.

In 1950, a tornado blew through Bedfordshire in England. The tornado plucked all the feathers off several chickens but they survived!

In 1979, a great rainbow appeared over North Wales. It was said that it lasted for three hours.

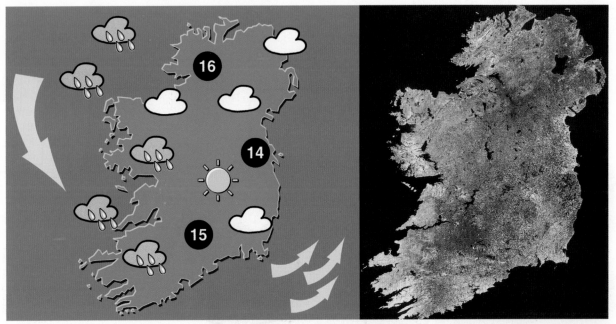

This is a picture of Ireland taken by a weather satellite.

Key

rain

sun

wind

cloud

snow

Weather sayings

- RED SKY IN THE MORNING, SHEPHERDS WARNING. RED SKY AT NIGHT SHEPHERDS DELIGHT.
- ST SWITHIN'S DAY IF THOU DOST RAIN, FOR FORTY DAYS IT WILL REMAIN; ST SWITHIN'S DAY IF THOU BE FAIR, FOR FORTY DAYS 'TWILL RAIN NAE MARE.

(If it rains on St Swithin's Day, on 15 July, it will rain for the next 40 days.)

- WHEN THE WIND IS OUT OF THE EAST, IT IS NEITHER GOOD FOR MAN NOR BEAST.
- A COLD NIGHT, STARS BRIGHT.

1. Look at the weather chart and give a weather report based on it.
2. Look or listen to today's weather forecast. Make your own weather chart based on what you have heard.
3. Find out more amazing weather facts.
4. Look up the meterological website: www.met.ie. Find out the weather for yesterday. Was it right?

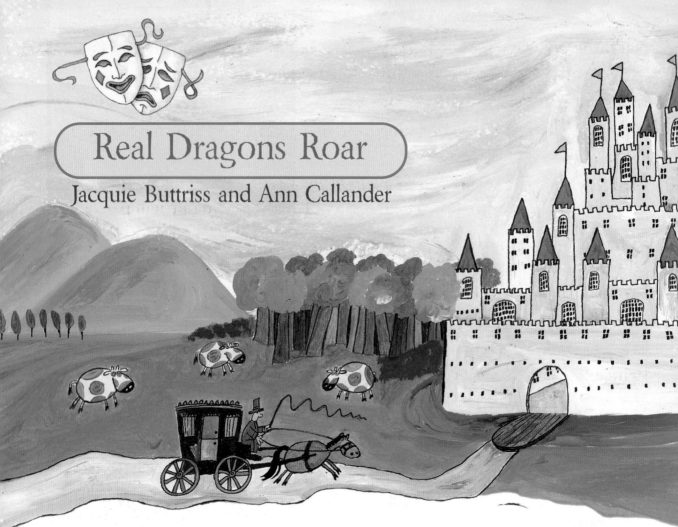

Real Dragons Roar

Jacquie Buttriss and Ann Callander

Narrator: Long ago, in a far away kingdom, there lived a dragon. But he wasn't an ordinary dragon. He was a very friendly dragon. He didn't breathe fire when strangers walked past his cave.

Dragon: I don't even smoke.

Narrator: He wore a pair of brightly coloured socks which he pulled right up to his scaly knees.

Dragon: I don't want my sharp claws to hurt anybody.

Narrator: And he never roared.

Dragon: (*covering his ears*) I hate loud noises.

Narrator: The dragon liked a quiet life. Best of all he liked reading books and eating fudge.

Dragon: Especially both at once!

CAST
Narrator
Dragon
Prince
Anna
Guard
Farmer

Narrator: The dragon had many friends but his best friends were a farmer and his clever daughter, Anna.

Dragon: She makes really good fudge.

Narrator: Now, in the same kingdom, there was a very selfish prince who lived in a castle.

Prince: I don't see why I should have to share things with anyone. After all, I'm a prince. The trouble is I'm bored. No one will play with me.

Guard: I'll play a game with you, Your Highness.

Prince: Oh, all right. Go and get the snakes and ladders.

Narrator: The guard went away and the prince stared out of the castle window.

Prince: (*looking fed up*) It's hopeless playing games with the guard. He gets everything wrong.

Narrator: Just then, the guard came back carrying a small ladder.

Guard: I couldn't find any snakes but I've found this ladder, Your Highness.

Prince: Oh no! Not that kind of ladder. I want the game of snakes and ladders.

Guard: I'm sorry, Your Highness. I'll go and look again.

Prince: No, don't bother. We'll play hide and seek instead.

Guard: Yes, Your Highness. I like hide and seek.

Prince: I'll go and hide, because I know all the best places. You count to 100.

Guard: But I can only count to 29, Your Highness.

Prince: Well, count to 29 very slowly.

Narrator: The guard began counting very slowly, while the prince ran off to hide.

Guard: 18... 19... 20... 29... coming!

Narrator: Meanwhile, the farmer and his daughter were planning to visit the dragon.

Farmer: Let's take the dragon some books to read and a basket of food.

Anna: I've made him some fudge too.

Narrator: So they set off to visit their friend, the dragon, but when they got to his cave, they found the dragon looking miserable.

Farmer: (*looking concerned*) What's the matter?

Anna: Aren't you well? I've brought you some fudge.

Dragon: Thank you.

Narrator: The dragon gave a big sigh and popped a piece of fudge into his mouth.

Farmer: Tell us why you are so sad.

Dragon: It was that book.

Farmer: What book?

Dragon: The one you gave me about St George.

Anna: Didn't you like it? I thought you might like to read about another dragon.

Farmer: Oh, don't worry. Nobody kills dragons nowadays.

Anna: Especially friendly dragons like you.

Dragon: Why is it always the knight who rescues the maiden in distress? Why can't a dragon rescue a maiden?

Farmer: I'm sure you could, but there aren't many maidens in distress around anymore.

Anna: Thank goodness!

Dragon: But I want to do something exciting, and be famous. I want to be a hero.

Narrator: He popped another piece of fudge in his mouth and a big tear rolled slowly down his scaly cheek.

Anna: Don't worry, Dragon. I'll go and pick some flowers to cheer you up.

Narrator: Meanwhile, back at the castle, the prince was bored. The guard came back.

Prince: What's the good of playing hide and seek if you don't come looking for me?

Guard: Oh, I forgot I was looking for you and I went off to hide.

Prince: You're no good at hide and seek. Oh, what can I do now?

Guard: We could play another game.

Prince: But you get them all wrong. No, I've got a better idea. Let's go for a ride and we can look for someone who is good at playing games.

Guard: Yes, Your Highness.

Prince: Go and tell the groom to saddle two horses.

Guard: At once, Your Highness.

Narrator The prince and the guard rode towards the village. They saw Anna picking some flowers.

Prince: (*pointing to Anna*) There's a girl over there. Perhaps she knows how to play games. Quick, go and talk to her.

Guard: What shall I say?

Prince: … um, you could ask her what time it is.

Guard: But we already know what time it is. My tummy's rumbling. It's tea time.

Prince: Never mind… I'll speak to her myself.

Narrator: The prince rode up to Anna.

Prince: Can you help us?

Anna: What is the matter?

Prince: My guard and I are looking for someone.

Anna: Who?

Prince: Someone who can play games better than anyone else in the kingdom.

Anna:	What kind of games?
Prince:	Well, I am particularly good at chess. Do you know anyone who plays chess?
Anna:	Yes, me! I like playing chess.
Prince:	Then I challenge you to a match at the castle.
Anna:	All right. But I must tell my father first.
Prince:	No. It's getting late. We must go now.
Anna:	But… but…
Prince:	Guard. Seize this girl and bring her back to the castle.
Guard:	Yes, Your Highness.
Anna:	Let me go. Help! (*loudly*)
Narrator:	Inside the cottage, Anna's father heard Anna shouting. He rushed outside.
Farmer:	Hey! What's happening? What are you doing with my daughter? Where are you taking her?
Narrator:	The Prince and the guard did not answer. They were already riding away towards the castle with Anna.
Farmer:	Oh, what shall I do?
Narrator:	The farmer thought hard and decided to go and see his friend, the dragon. The dragon was sitting in his cave darning his spare socks.
Farmer:	You must help Anna. The prince and the guard have taken her away to the castle.
Dragon:	That's dreadful. But what can I do?
Farmer:	You can rescue her.
Dragon:	Who, me?
Farmer:	Yes, You are the only one who can help her.
Dragon:	You mean she's a maiden in distress?
Farmer:	Yes.
Narrator:	The dragon was delighted. Here was his big chance to be a hero.
Dragon:	But… how?

Farmer: Here, I've brought a book about dragons. Perhaps that will give us some ideas.

Dragon: I hope so!

Narrator: They looked at the dragon book together and read about all the things that a dragon can do.

Farmer: It says here that you can terrify people with your sharp claws.

Dragon: (*taking off his socks*) Can I really? I'd better take off my socks, and see what I can do.

Farmer: My goodness! Your claws are frightening!

Dragon: What else can I do?

Farmer: You can roar so loudly that people will run and hide.

Narrator: The dragon opened his mouth and gave a great roar. The farmer was so frightened he ran to hide behind a tree.

Dragon: Come back here! I'm just starting to enjoy myself. What else does it say in the book?

Farmer: It says here that you can breathe flames.

Narrator: The dragon took a deep breath and blew such enormous flames that they burnt the grass outside his cave. He was so surprised that he nearly fell over!

Dragon: Wow! I didn't know I could do that!

Farmer: Well done. You never know what you can do until you try.

Dragon: That's what my teacher used to tell me at dragon school. But I never believed her!

Farmer: Come on then. Now we must go and rescue Anna.

Dragon: I think I'd better have a piece of fudge first.

Narrator: The dragon and the farmer set off together for the castle. They walked up to the huge castle door.

Farmer: How shall we get through this thick wooden door?

Dragon: Don't worry. I'll burn it down. Just watch!

Narrator: The dragon blew with all his might and the door disappeared in a burst of flames.

Farmer: Well done!

Narrator: Then the guard began to shoot arrows at the dragon. But the dragon roared so loudly…

Dragon: ROAR!

Narrator: … that the guard ran away to hide.

Guard: (*running away*) Help!

Farmer: Look. Here comes the prince with a huge silver sword.

Prince: You might frighten the guards, but you don't frighten me!

Narrator: The dragon's knees trembled.

Dragon: (*popping a piece of fudge in his mouth*) I think I'd better have another piece of fudge.

Narrator: Then the dragon remembered he was a fierce dragon and he showed his sharp claws and he roared loudly…

Dragon: ROAR!

Prince: You d-d-d-don't frighten me.

Narrator: Then he blew fiery flames at the prince. The prince's coat caught fire.

Prince: Help! Help! (*loudly!*)

Narrator: The guard heard the prince's cries and ran over to the well. He filled a bucket of water and threw it over the prince.

Prince: Thank you, Guard. What a clever thing to do. You saved my life.

Narrator: Meanwhile, the dragon and the farmer rushed into the castle to look for Anna. She was sitting in a velvet chair and looking down at a chess board.

Farmer: Anna!

Anna: Shhh! I'm trying to concentrate.

Dragon: Anna! I've come to save you.

Anna: Oh, Dragon. Don't be so old-fashioned. Can't you see I can look after myself?

Dragon: But I roared a terrible roar and showed my sharp claws and I blew fiery flames at the prince.

Anna: I wondered what all the noise was about. But now be sensible and put your socks back on. The prince and I are in the middle of a game of chess.

Narrator: From that day on, the prince and Anna became very good friends. The prince forgot all about being selfish and he started to be kind instead.

Dragon: The guard and I are very good friends too.

Guard: Yes, and the dragon always shares his fudge with me.

Narrator: So, Anna, the prince, the dragon, the guard and the farmer all lived happily ever after.

Anna: If you believe that you'll believe anything.

Records in the world of nature

1. Do you know any records about people, music, sport or nature?

The largest animal of all is the blue whale. It grows to 30 metres in length and is bigger than even the largest dinosaurs.

The biggest land animal in the world is the African elephant. It grows to a height of over three metres and weighs nearly six tonnes. The elephant spends more than 20 hours a day feeding. In an elephant herd, it is always the female that rules. One African elephant can weigh more than 100 people.

The fastest animal in the world is the cheetah. It can run up to 100 kilometres an hour, but only over short distances.

The tortoise lives longer than any other animal. It can live for up to 200 years. A tortoise would need a very big birthday cake for all its candles!

The smallest mammal is the pygmy shrew. It weighs only 2.5 grams and is only seven centimetres long. It eats its own weight in worms and insects every day.

The strongest smelling animal is the zorilla. It can be smelled from a distance of over 1.5 kilometres.

The bee hummingbird is the smallest bird in the world. It is called a bee hummingbird because of the humming sound that its wings make and because it is not much bigger than a bee.

The squid has the largest eye of any animal. It is 16 times wider than a human's eye.

The laziest animal in the world is the sloth. It sleeps for about 16 hours a day, hanging upside-down from a tree. The sloth is also the slowest animal in the world. In trees it covers about five metres in one minute. On the ground it moves about two metres in one minute.

The mammal that makes the most noise is the howler monkey. Its call can be heard up to five kilometres away.

The tallest animal is the giraffe. The giraffe measures six metres in height, higher than a double-decker bus. The giraffe needs a large heart to pump blood all the way up its long neck, which can be 2.4 metres long.

For its size, the rhino beetle is the strongest animal on earth. It can move an object 850 times its own weight.

The shrew eats its own body weight in bugs, slugs and grubs every day. That's the same as a person eating about 2,500 hamburgers in one day!

The millipede has more legs than any other creature, but it doesn't really have 1,000 legs. The most legs ever counted on one millipede was 750.

The reticulated python (or retic) is the longest snake in the world. It measures nine metres in length, about as long as a bus.

The Gaboon viper has hollow teeth that pump venom into the snake's victim. It has the longest fangs of any snake. One bite contains enough venom to kill 10 people.

Ready! Steady! Go!

Sloth 120 metres/h

Elephant 25 km/h

Iguana 34.9 km/h

Man 37 km/h

The albatross is the biggest of all seabirds. It has the greatest wingspan of any bird, measuring three metres from one outstretched wing tip to the other.

The Andean condor, a type of vulture, is the biggest bird of prey. It weighs about 15 kilograms.

The saltwater crocodile is the largest reptile in the world. It weighs as much as three cars and grows to be three times longer than your bed!

The ostrich is the largest bird in the world. It can run as fast as a horse. It uses its small wings to help it keep its balance when it runs.

1. What was your favourite animal fact? Say why.
2. Choose one of these creatures and make a fact map about it. (Look back at the fact map on page 70.)
3. Which animal is the a.) laziest b.) slowest c.) strongest d.) fastest?

Pronghorn 67 km/h

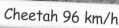

Cheetah 96 km/h

Sailfish 109 km/h

Peregrine Falcon 200 km/h

The Dinosaur's Dinner

June Crebbin

Once a mighty dinosaur
Came to dine with me,
He gobbled up the curtains
And swallowed our settee.

He didn't seem to fancy
Onion soup with crusty bread,
He much preferred the flavour
Of our furniture instead.

He ate up all our dining chairs
And carpets from the floor,
He polished off the table, then
He looked around for more.

The television disappeared
In one almighty gulp,
Wardrobes, beds and bathroom
He crunched into a pulp.

He really loved the greenhouse,
He liked the garden shed,
He started on the chimney pots
But then my mother said:

Your friends are always welcome
To drop in for a bite,
But really this one seems to have
A giant appetite.

You'd better take him somewhere else,
I'm sure I don't know where,
I only know this friend of yours
Needs more than we can spare!

And suddenly I realised
I knew the very place,
And when I showed him where it was
You should have seen his face –

I don't think I've seen anyone
Enjoy a dinner more,
I watched him wander on his way,
A happy dinosaur!

The council did rebuild our school,
But that of course took time...
And all because a dinosaur
Came home with me to dine!

Allosaurus

Jack Prelutsky

Allosaurus liked to bite,
its teeth were sharp as sabres,
it frequently, with great delight,
made mincemeat of its neighbours.

Allosaurus liked to hunt,
and when it caught its quarry,
it tore it open, back and front,
and never said, 'I'm sorry!'

Allosaurus liked to eat,
and using teeth and talons,
it stuffed itself with tons of meat,
and guzzled blood by gallons.

Allosaurus liked to munch,
and kept from growing thinner
by gnawing an enormous lunch,
then rushing off to dinner.

DINO EGG

Charlie James

Bill and Ned Finn live with their sister Stacey and their parents. One morning when they were having breakfast, Ned's egg started making a TAP, TAP, TAP sound. Then it began to glow and change colour. Next thing the shell split open.

Chapter two: Eggs-plosion
Silence:
Some thing was <u>clambering</u> out of the egg cup. It had:

1 NARROW HEAD with a GREEN FEATHERY CREST

1 ROUND PINK BODY with PURPLE SPOTS

2 HUGE EYES Tight shut

1 long WHIP-LIKE tail

3 SHARP CLAWS on every paw

and a TRULY TERRIBLE Smell!

'Bill,' I <u>squeaked</u>, covering my nose to block out a stench worse than Stacey's hairspray, '*what* exactly is *that*?'
'Well,' said Bill, craning his neck round the pot plant for a better view. 'I'm not exactly sure, but... judging from its profile, lower tibia formation and tail, I think it might be... a... Tyrannosaurus[1] rex!' ⭐

⭐ Do you know the names of any other dinosaurs?

[1] Pronounced Tie-RAN-oh-sore-us

91

I groaned. Bill is mad about dinosaurs. He may only be six, but once on the subject he sounds like a professional palaeontologist[2] – an expert dino-bore. He spends hours talking about them, drawing them and playing pretend fights with them. He's as obsessed with the wretched things as Dad is with fish, Stacey with clothes and Mum with knitting. But if Bill was convinced we'd just witnessed the birth of our very own Jurassic Park, I was not.

'Believe it or not, Ned,' he whispered, 'the T. Rex was the *King* of the dinosaurs – one of the meanest meat-eating machines ever to have walked the planet. According to my books, it weighed eight tonnes, grew up to twelve metres long and might have run as fast as sixty-four kilometres per hour – that's about *eighteen metres per second*. Its specially-hinged jaws meant that its bite was five hundred and thirty times more powerful than any living creature. Why, it could probably crush cars with its teeth!' There was a pause. 'Hey, Ned,' Bill added brightly, popping his head through the leaves, 'do you think Mum would let me keep it as a pet?'

'No!' I snapped.

'And why not?'

'Because,' I muttered, keeping one eye on *The Thing* on the table, 'dinosaurs are dead, deceased, defunct, extinct! That is *not* a dinosaur. *That* is a mutant duck!' And feeling rather pleased at having solved the mystery, I picked up my chair and sat down. ✦

'A *duck*?'

'Of course. After all, it has feathers and a crest. And besides, whoever's heard of a pink T. Rex?'

'No one, but that doesn't mean they didn't exist,' sniffed Bill. 'Tell you what, if you really think that creature's a duck, why don't you give it your toast?'

I hesitated, but, as I wanted to prove Bill wrong, I picked up the toast and edged towards the creature with my hand outstretched. I must admit it looked rather cute, lolling against the side of the egg cup with its eyes still closed.

'Tch, tch, tch,' I whispered, making the sound that Mum does when she's looking at something small and helpless.

'Tch, tch, Yum,' replied the sightless dinosaur, obviously thinking the same

What does 'mutant' mean?

[2] Pronounced Pal-ay-on-tol-o-jist

thing. Then, to my horror, it started to move. First it stretched out its neck. It stretched it out a long, **long** way. Then it stretched out its left leg and then its right. Finally it opened its jaws to show a double row of jagged, white teeth.

'B-B-Bill', I stuttered. 'Did you see those...?'

'Fangs? Yes, aren't they cool? *Really* sharp. Do you know what that means?'

'That it's a vampire?' I quavered, as the duck spattered great gobs of gooey saliva over the table.

'No,' laughed Bill, emerging from behind the pot plant. 'That it really *is* a dinosaur. You can tell by its teeth. Have I ever told you how they came in all sorts of shapes and sizes? Daggers, knives, pegs, combs, rakes...'

But I wasn't listening. I was looking at the dino-duck. It was moving across the table – directly towards us. 'B-B-Bill', I stuttered, 'w-watch out...'

But Bill was too busy talking to listen. On and on he went. On and on and on and on, waving his hands around and completely forgetting that something strange with sharp teeth was crawling towards him. 'Believe it or not, Ned, some plant-eaters – or herbivores as they are known – had pencil- or spoon-shaped teeth with angled tops so that they could pull leaves into their mouths and chew them more easily...'

The creature piled the remains of Dad's bacon into its mouth and chewed it up along with one of my socks. 'B-Bill', I whimpered. 'On the other hand, meat-eaters, or carnivores,' he continued, 'had sharp, spiky fangs which were specially designed to tear through skin, rip flesh and crush the bones of their victims. Tell you what, hand me another bit of toast and I'll creep forward and see if I can get a better look.'

Why is Bill not afraid?

'No way!' I shouted. 'Bill, don't you understand? That dinosaur doesn't want to eat your bread. It wants to eat you!' And gibbering with fear, I leapt forward to save him from becoming the first fine feast of a famished feathered fossil.

Which was a really bad mistake.

For just then, the dinosaur opened its eyes and jumped onto my neck, shouting:

'Mum!'

1. How does Bill describe the T. Rex?
2. Bill is obsessed with dinosaurs. What are other members of the family obsessed with?
3. What happens when the dinosaur opens its eyes?

4. The author likes to use words starting with the same letter in sentences, e.g. 'Meanest meat-eating machine'. Can you find other examples?
5. Bill tells us that the T. Rex is 'king' of dinosaurs. What makes it the king?
6. What was the most interesting dino fact that you learned?

7. What do you think Ned's Mum and Dad will say when they find out what has happened?
8. What might happen next? Say why.
9. Can you think of another title for the chapter?
10. How do the two brothers react differently to the dinosaur?

11. Bill thinks the dino is a T. Rex because of its 'tibia formation'. What is the tibia? Can you name other bones in the body?
12. What does a palaeontologist do?
13. Do you have any 'obsessions'?

DINO EGG

Charlie James

Dinosaurs

1. Talk about dinosaurs.
2. Which is your favourite?

Terrible lizards

The word dinosaur means terrible lizard. Dinosaurs were large reptiles with tough scaly skins that roamed Earth millions of years ago. Some dinosaurs had sharp claws and teeth and they fed on other animals. These were carnivores. Some dinosaurs ate only plants and leaves. These were herbivores. Only a small number of dinosaurs were omnivores, meaning they ate both plants and animals like most humans do today.

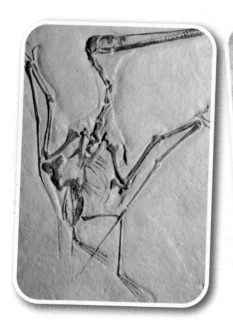

Fossils

If dinosaurs lived so long ago, how do we know so much about them? The answer lies in fossils. They have been found on every continent, even the Antarctic. Fossils are the remains of plants and animals that are found deep in the ground. Scientists can piece together clues about the lives of the dinosaurs, what

95

...looked like, how big they were and even when and where they lived. They can work out a dinosaur's weight and speed by measuring the depth of fossil footprints and the distance between the footprints.

The biggest dinosaur footprint ever discovered was found near Salt Lake City in the United States of America. It was one metre 36 centimetres long.

The biggest dinosaur footprint

Mary Anning: fossil expert

About 200 years ago, a girl called Mary Anning was living in England. Mary was only 11 years old when she discovered the first fossil — the Ichthyosaur. After her fantastic find she grew up to become a great fossil expert called a palaeontologist. So far, fossils of over 350 different kinds of dinosaur have been discovered and new ones are being identified all of the time.

Carnivores

Carnivores hunted in packs making it easier to overpower their victims. They could move quickly and surround their prey making it difficult for their victim to escape. Some had strong claws on their short arms or on their long back legs. These were useful for gripping their victims while they sank their enormous teeth into their prey.

The Tyrannosaurus Rex

Perhaps the most terrifying of all the dinosaurs was Tyrannosaurus Rex —

the king of the dinosaurs. T. Rex was up to 16 metres long. This is about as long as five cars placed in a row! T. Rex grew to six metres high (about the height of a two storey house). It could run very fast on its powerful hind legs. Its mouth was big enough to swallow you whole and its large sharp teeth helped to rip its prey to

The Velociraptor

shreds. Velociraptor (vell-oss-i-rap-tor) was a smaller carnivore than T. Rex, but it could run faster. The hooked claw in the middle of each foot was its main weapon.

Herbivores

Most herbivores travelled in large herds. They were always on the move looking for food.

The Triceratops

Some had sharp bones on their heads to protect themselves from the fierce meat-eaters. Triceratops (try-ser-a-tops) had a huge head with three large horns and a bony frill and liked to charge at its attackers. Some dinosaurs, like Ankylosaurus (ankle-o-sore-us) were built like an army tank. It had armoured plates all over the top of its body. These were so hard that predators could break their teeth on them!

The Ankylosaurus

Other herbivores were huge and had long necks that could reach up to the tops of tall trees. Here they fed on the highest leaves and branches, just as giraffes do today. Brachiosaurus (brak-ee-oh-sore-us) could stretch its head

The Apatosaurus

up to a height of 12 metres —as high as a three-storey house. Apatosaurus (a-pat-oh-sore-us), did not chew its food but swallowed stones which helped to grind the food down in his stomach.

Stegosaurus (steg-oh-sore-us) was different from most other herbivores; it liked to live on its own. It had enormous back legs which were twice as long as its front legs. The double row of plates on its back made it look fierce. These were not sharp, but its razor-sharp spiky tail was deadly.

The Brachiosaurus

The Stegosaurus

Extinction

About 65 million years ago the dinosaurs vanished off the earth. Nobody knows for sure what happened to them. One idea is that the climate changed after a giant meteor shower. When these huge meteor rocks crashed to Earth, they threw up massive clouds of dust. This blocked out the sun for a long time and caused plants to die. Like the snakes and reptiles that live in hot countries today, dinosaurs were cold-blooded animals. They too needed heat from the sun to keep their bodies warm.

Another idea is that the weather at this time began to become colder. Some plants and animals began to die and there was less food around for the dinosaurs to eat. Little by little, life became harder for the dinosaurs and soon they became extinct.

Did you know?

Which dinosaur was the smallest?

The smallest dinosaur was the Compsognathus. It was about the size of a chicken. It had long bony legs. It was very fast on its feet and fed on small animals. Its long tail helped it to balance. Its thigh bone was only 11 cm long, less than half the length of your ruler.

Which dinosaur was the longest?

Diplodocus stretched to 27 metres. That's about the length of a swimming pool! Its neck was almost half that length. It was too big to go into the forest. It is thought it poked its long neck in amongst the trees to peck at the leaves and branches. Its long tail helped it to balance.

Which dinosaur was known as the egg thief?

Oviraptor means egg thief. It is one of the few known omnivores. It was thought that it mostly ate eggs because the first fossil was found on top of some eggs. It probably used the two sharp spikes inside its powerful beak to crack open other dinosaurs' eggs before sucking out their contents.

Which was the most unusual eater?

The fossil of Gallimimus was discovered in 2001. It had no teeth. The fossil shows that it ate by sieving tiny bits of food through comb-like plates in its mouth.

1. What does the word dinosaur mean?
2. Can you think of any another reason why dinosaurs might have died out?
3. Name all the dinosaurs mentioned in the passage. Can you add to the list?
4. Find out about another extinct or endangered animal.

Specky Becky Bucks

John Quinn

Rebecca Buckley is known as Becky Bucks. Sometimes people call her Specky Becky Bucks, because she wears glasses. She hates that. Becky loves Gaelic Football and her dream is to play in Croke Park one day – just like her Grandad did. When Becky's Granny becomes ill, Becky travels to London with her parents and brothers ET and Simon to visit her in hospital.

Chapter nine: Grandad

Later that day, we met up with Grandad. Mum stayed on in the hospital with Granny.

'Right,' Dad said, checking his watch, 'Next stop – "The Future is Now" – an amazing exhibition in Earl's Court.'

ET's eyes lit up.

'Would you like to come, Grandad?'

Grandad had gone very quiet again.

'Ah, no. I think I'll give it a miss. I'm not too bothered about the future just now, so if you don't mind –'

'Grandad and I have a date in the park,' I blurted out suddenly. When I said it, I couldn't believe I'd said it.

'But Becky...' Dad was taken aback. 'This is all about your future, the world you're going to grow up in...'

'It's all right, Becky. You go with your Dad,' Grandad said.

'No, I WANT to go to the park with you, Grandad. New tricks – remember?'

Grandad smiled. It was settled. As far as I was concerned my future was now, in the park with Grandad.

Why do you think Grandad said that he was not too bothered about the future?

We sat on a bench in the park watching squirrels scuttling across the grass and up and down trees.

'Them boys can run, Becky. Look at them! If you could run like them no-one would catch you on the pitch, would they?'

'No way. Tell me about playing in Croke Park, Grandad.'

'Oh now, who has been telling stories! That was a long time ago – over fifty years. I was only seventeen, playing for Meath minors in the Leinster Championship Final. And Croke Park was nothing like it is today. But it was wonderful – to go out and play where my heroes played – Peter McDermott and Frankie Byrne. I loved every minute of it.

I wished it would go on forever. And I scored two points. The only problem was – WE LOST! But sure, that's the way of the world, Becky. That's the way of the world.'

'But did you never play there again?'

'No. Got a pile of injuries and was out of action for a few years and then...'

'And then?'

'And then I met... and then I met... your Granny...'

'And then?'

'Oh but you are the curious one, Becky! And then the problem was a job! It was very hard to get a job then – so Granny and I got married and went off to London. Drove a bus for forty years – and here I am!'

How do you think Croke Park might have looked 50 years ago?

'You drove a bus for forty years and you played in Croke Park! Cool! My dream is to play in Croke Park – maybe drive a bus too!'

'Well, you just hold on to your dreams, Becky. You never know!'

Grandad reached into a shopping bag. 'Now, that's enough talk. Time for some action!'

He took out a beautiful football. Not plastic. Real leather.

'I got this for you earlier. Now let's see some Shannon style.'

'I hope Mrs Pratt never gets her hands on this ball,' I said, tipping it from toe to hand.

'Mrs Pratt?'

I told him about our neighbour and her hydrangeas and her savage dog.

'Well, Becky, if you learn how to control and kick the ball properly, Mrs Pratt will never even get a smell of it,' Grandad laughed.

'I hope not. It does smell lovely and leathery.'

For the next twenty minutes we played serious stuff. Grandad went in goals (two coats) and I took shots. We practised hand-passes, foot-passes, hitting the ball with the outside of the foot, blocking a kick, hitting a target (a huge elm tree) – and solo runs, except that I didn't need to practise them. Even with ordinary shoes I amazed Grandad with my solo runs.

'You're teaching me now, Becky, for sure. Where did you learn to solo like that?' he gasped.

'Don't know. I just sort of taught myself. Mum says it's in the blood.'

'Maybe she's right, but I could never solo like that! Do it again!' ✫

✫ Do you think Grandad and Becky get on well? Why do you think this?

I did. Again. And again. And again.

'Brilliant!' Grandad said. 'Now I have only one more trick to show you – the shimmy!'

'The sh-shimmy?'

'The shimmy. Now watch me. I'm a forward coming in with the ball. You're a back. Try to stop me!'

Some chance, I thought – with the size of him and the size of me – but I moved forward to try and get the ball.

Suddenly he was gone the other way, right past me.

'How did you do that?' I gasped.

'That was the shimmy! Watch again!'

He showed the ball and then did a little trick with his feet, like a step we do in Irish dancing. Then he was gone the other way.

'One more time! Watch closely now!' He did the shimmy again. It seemed easy when he did it. He handed me the ball. 'Now it's your turn!'

Of course I tripped and fell in a heap (like Simon) the first time I tried it.

'Don't worry! Try again!' He didn't even laugh.

I tried again. At least I didn't fall this time. I kept trying. All the time Grandad kept praising me.

'You have it now... That's nice... Try another one...'

And then, I could do it – almost like him.

'Good girl! There'll be no stopping you now! ✫

Do you know what they used to call me when I was a young fellow, Becky?'

'The Shimmy?' I guessed.

'Nearly right,' he laughed. 'I was called "Jimmy the Shimmy"! Jimmy Shannon – "Jimmy the Shimmy". Many's the fellow I made a fool of with the shimmy. Maybe they'll call you "Becky the Shimmy" now!'

✫ Grandad encourages Becky a lot. Find examples in the story so far.

103

It didn't sound as good as 'Jimmy the Shimmy'.

Grandad looked at his watch. 'Time to go, Becky. We have to meet your Mum.'

We walked back to the hospital. Grandad took my hand and we skipped along, playing a game of 'Don't Walk on the Lines'! Grandad laughed as I tried to avoid the lines on the path. Just when it seemed I could not avoid a line, I had a brilliant idea. I did a shimmy and danced over the line.

'Ah brilliant, Becky, brilliant! You're a star!' He ruffled my hair. 'Do you know what I'm going to tell you?'

'Hardly, Grandad!'

'I don't know when I had such fun. And you took my mind off ... You took my mind off – things. God bless you, child.'

He squeezed my hand until it hurt, but I didn't mind. We had reached the hospital. I knew what he was thinking about: Granny.

Mum was waiting for us. She looked sad and her eyes were red.

'I thought you two had forgotten about me,' she said, almost in a whisper.

'Becky and me had some important business in the park,' Grandad explained, giving me a big wink.

Mum looked down at my feet. 'Becky, look at the state of your shoes! What on earth were you up to?'

'It's only a bit of muck. Clean muck!' Grandad explained.

'I can do the shimmy, Mum. "Jimmy the Shimmy" showed me!'

She looked at me and then at Grandad. 'Honestly! I don't know which of you is worse!' she sighed as she searched in her handbag for a tissue to clean my shoes. At least she was smiling now.

Why do you think Mum was so sad?

1. For which team did Grandad play in Croke Park?
2. What job did Grandad have in London?
3. Why did Grandad never play in Croke Park again?

4. What kind of person is Becky? Why do you think this?
5. Grandad and Becky enjoyed each other's company. Find examples to show this.
6. Scan the text. What do you learn about Mum in this extract?

7. 'Mum says it's in the blood'. What did Mum mean?
8. How did Becky help to lift Grandad's spirits?
9. How do you know Becky's brother wanted to go to 'The Future is Now' exhibition?
10. What might happen next in the story? Give a reason for your answer

11. Do you have a talent that is 'in your blood'?
12. Grandad told Becky to hold on to her dreams. What dreams do you have for the future?
13. Have you ever been to Croke Park or to any sports stadium? Talk about it.

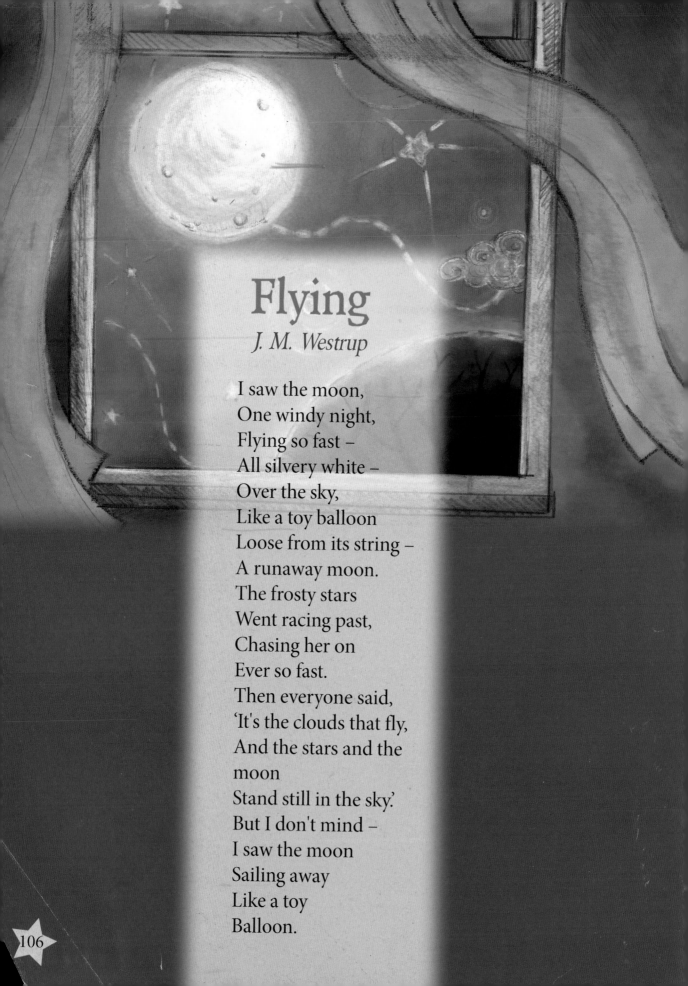

Flying

J. M. Westrup

I saw the moon,
One windy night,
Flying so fast –
All silvery white –
Over the sky,
Like a toy balloon
Loose from its string –
A runaway moon.
The frosty stars
Went racing past,
Chasing her on
Ever so fast.
Then everyone said,
'It's the clouds that fly,
And the stars and the
moon
Stand still in the sky.'
But I don't mind –
I saw the moon
Sailing away
Like a toy
Balloon.

Did you know?

The Moon is about 380,000 kilometres away from the Earth. If you could walk to the Moon, it would take you almost 10 years to get there.

The Moon is 3,500 kilometres across. This makes it big enough to cover Australia.

By 1972, 12 people had landed on the Moon. The third person on the 1969 Moon mission was astronaut Michael Collins. He did not get to stand on the Moon. Nobody has landed on the Moon since.

The Moon travels around Earth in a path called an *orbit*. The Moon orbits the earth once a month.

Astronauts on the Moon travelled around in a kind of car called a moonbuggy. The moonbuggy had a TV camera to take photographs and bags to collect rock samples. The moonbuggy would not break any speed limits. It could only travel up to a speed of 18 kilometres an hour!

Gravity is the force that pulls an object down to the ground. The Moon's gravity is only one-sixth the gravity of the Earth. If you could jump one metre high on the Earth, you would be able to jump six metres high on the Moon! Astronauts had to practise hard to be able to walk on the Moon because they were so light.

There is no air on the Moon. Astronauts had to wear special spacesuits to let them breathe. The spacesuits had lots of tubes and took 45 minutes to put on!

Sound needs air to travel through so the Moon is totally silent. Astronauts on the Moon had to use radios to talk to each other even when they were right beside each other. Neil Armstrong's footprints are still on the Moon because there is no air to disturb them!

1. What is a satellite?
2. Imagine you are an astronaut. Talk about your most exciting adventure in space.
3. What do you think life on the Moon might be like in the future?
4. Make up questions of your own about the Moon. Ask your friend to answer them.

The Legend of the Worst Boy in the World

Eoin Colfer

Chapter one: It's Not Fair

I have four brothers, and they are always complaining about something. If I ever have a problem, and I go to my mum to talk about it, there are generally at least two brothers in the queue before me, moaning about something totally stupid. I could have an actual problem like a hangnail or a missing sock, and there they are wasting Mum's time with silly stuff like jam on their faces or back-to-front jumpers.

My four brothers have their favourite problems that they like to moan about at least once a day. Mum calls these problems their *hobby horses.* Whenever they start whinging about them, Dad makes horsey noises and a

here-we-go-again face, but Mum listens anyway because she's our mum.

Marty is the oldest brother, and his hobby horse is that he's never allowed to do anything, and he might as well be in prison.

'Why can't I have a motorbike?' he often whines. 'I'm ten now and that's nearly sixteen. If I had a helmet on, the police would never notice.'

Or another one is: 'Why can't I have a full-sized snooker table in the garage? It's only full of old tools and a car, nothing important. I'll pay for the snooker table as soon as I become a famous football player.'

Dad sometimes comes into a room just to hear Marty complain about something. He says that Marty is far more entertaining than any television show.

'Snooker table,' Dad chuckles. 'Marty, my boy. You are cracking me up.'

This is not what Marty wants to hear, so he storms off sulking. Once when Marty came back after storming off, Dad presented him with a cardboard Oscar for best actor.

My name is Will and I'm the next in line.

After me comes my second brother, Donnie, whose hobby horse is his hair. No matter how often Mum washes or combs it, there's always something wrong.

'It's sticking up at the back, Mum.' So mum flattens the back.

'Now, Donnie, off you go.'

'It's still sticking up, Mum.'

'No, it isn't. You're having hair hallucinations, Donnie. Go on now, you'll be late for school.'

'I can see a hair sticking up. It's definitely there. The girls will see, and I'll get a nickname. Sticky-Up Woodman they'll call me. It'll be horrible.'

And so Mum gets out a water bottle and sprays Donnie's head.

'Better?'

'I suppose.'

This happens every second day. On the other days, Donnie wants his hair to stick up, because he thinks it's cool.

Brothers three and four, Bert and HP, have invented brand-new words so that they can whinge more efficiently. Bert's new word is 'canniva', as in 'Canniva bar of chocolate?'

> ★ What kind of person is Dad, do you think?

'Not before your dinner, honey,' says Mum.

'Canniva square, just one square.'

'No, honey. Dinner's on the way.'

'Canniva bag of crisps then?'

'I think you're missing the point, Bert. No sweets or crisps before your dinner.'

'Canniva throat sweet?'

'Throat sweets are still sweets, honey.' Mum has great patience. Dad only puts up with two 'cannivas' before he gets annoyed.

HP (Half Pint) is the youngest and hates being the baby. The word he invented to complain about this is 'snoffair', as in: 'Snoffair. Chrissy's mummy allowed him to get his head shaved, now he looks at least five and a half.' He said this one afternoon after his half-day in baby infants.

'I'm not in charge of Chrissy,' said Mum. 'I'm only in charge of you. And I say, no head shaving.'

'Snoffair,' howled HP. 'Barry has a stick-on tattoo, like the big boys.'

'No stick-on tattoo. We've talked about this.'

'Snoffair,' muttered HP, then: 'What about an earring then? Loads of people have those. Snoffair that I don't have one.'

'Life's not fair sometimes,' said Mum, and hugs HP until he starts sucking his thumb. Two minutes later he is fast asleep.

Sometimes HP talks in his sleep. Guess what he says...

What other 'canniva' question might Bert ask?

All this complaining means that by the time Marty and I get home from school with our troubles there is usually a little brother perched on each of Mum's knees, moaning about their baby problems. And even if, miracle of miracles, there is a free knee, Mum is usually on auto-nod by then anyway. Auto-nod is when grown-ups don't really listen to what a child says; they just nod every five seconds or so until the child goes away.

So Marty and I decided that we had to target another grown-up to talk to about our own problems. Dad was the next target, but sometimes he works so late that we don't even see him before bedtime. Marty reckoned that Dad only had time for one set of complaints, and that set should be his. So I had to pick someone else. Somebody who was a good listener and had a lot of spare time. I knew just the person.

Grandad.

> ☆ Why does Mum go on auto-nod?

1. What do the letters H P stand for?
2. Name two things that Marty would like to have.
3. Who is telling the story?

4. Name the children from eldest to youngest.
5. Skim through the extract. Which of the brothers' complaints do you think is a.) the silliest b.) the funniest?
6. Mum has great patience with the children. Can you find examples of this?

7. How would you react if you were Mum?
8. What do you think Grandad will say to Will?
9. Do you think Mum finds Dad's comments helpful? Why do you think this?

10. Have you ever put on an Oscar-winning performance for your parents? Talk about it.
11. Who do you go to when you have a complaint to make?
12. Can you think of other funny words like 'Canniva' and 'Snoffair'?

EOIN COLFER
The Legend of
THE WORST
BOY
IN THE
WORLD

1. Have you heard of Judy Moody before? Tell the class about her.
2. Read the chapter title. What do you think it means?
3. What do you think Judy will do to save the world?

Judy Moody Saves the World!

Megan McDonald

Judy lives with her Mum, Dad and younger brother Stink. She wants to be a doctor when she grows up. In school she's been learning about the importance of the rainforest and that plants used for medicines grow there. Now she wants to help save the rainforests and the world.

A Mr Rubbish Mood

It was still dark out when Judy woke up early the next morning. She found her flashlight and notebook. Then she tiptoed downstairs to the kitchen and started to save the world.

She hoped she could save the world before breakfast. Judy wondered if other people making the world a better place had to do it quietly, and in the dark, so their parents would not wake up.

She, Judy Moody, was in a Mr Rubbish mood. Mr Rubbish was the Good Garbage Gremlin in Stink's comic book, who built his house out of French-fry cartons and pop bottles. He recycled everything, even lollipop sticks. And he never used anything from the rainforest.

Hmm... things that came from the rainforest. That would be a good place to start. Rubber came from the rainforest. And chocolate and spices and things like perfume. Even chewing gum.

Judy collected stuff from around the house and piled it on the kitchen table. Chocolate bars, brownie mix, vanilla ice cream. Her dad's coffee beans. The rubber toilet plunger. Gum from Stink's gumball machine. Her mum's lipstick from the bottom of her purse. She was so busy saving the rainforest that she didn't hear her family come into the kitchen.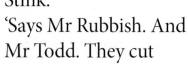

'What in the world...?' Mum said.

'Judy, why are you in the dark?' Dad asked, turning on the lights.

'Hey, my gumball machine!' Stink said.

Judy held out her arms to block the way. 'We're not going to use this stuff any more. It's all from the rainforest,' she told them.

'Says who?' asked Stink.

'Says Mr Rubbish. And Mr Todd. They cut down way too many trees to grow coffee and give us make-up and chewing gum. Mr Todd says the earth is our home. We have to take action to save it. We don't need all this stuff.'

'I need gum!' yelled Stink. 'Give me back my gum!'

'Stink! Don't yell. Haven't you ever heard of noise pollution?'

'Is my coffee in there?' Dad asked, rubbing his hair.

'Judy? Is that ice cream? It's dripping all over the table!' Mum carried the leaky carton over to the sink.

'ZZZZZZ-ZZZZZZZZ!' Judy made the sound of a chainsaw cutting down trees.

'She's batty,' Stink said.

Dad put the brownie mix back in the cupboard. Mum took the toilet plunger off the kitchen table and headed for the bathroom.

What have these things got to do with the rainforest?

Time for Plan B. Project RECYCLE. She, Judy Moody, would show her family just how much they hurt the planet. Every time someone threw something away, she would write it down. She got her notebook and looked in the trash can. She wrote down:

1 orange juice can
1 inside of peanut butter jar lid
1 plastic bread bag
4 broken eggshells
smelly yucky wet coffee grounds
3 paper muffin holders
2 smooshed Scarlett O'cherry juice boxes (and straws!)
½ bowl of oatmeal

'Stink! You shouldn't throw gooey old oatmeal in the trash!' Judy said.
'Dad! Tell her to quit spying on me.'
'I'm a Garbage Detective!' said Judy. '*Garbologist* to you. Mr Todd says if you want to learn what to recycle, you have to get to know your garbage.'
'Here,' said Stink, sticking something wet and mushy under Judy's nose. 'Get to know my apple core.'
'Hardee-har-har,' said Judy. 'Hasn't anybody in this family ever heard of the three Rs?'
'The three Rs?' asked Dad.
'Re-use. Re-cycle.'
'What's the third one?' asked Stink.
'Re-fuse to talk to little brothers until they quit throwing stuff away.'
'Mum! I'm not going to stop throwing stuff away just because Judy's having a trash attack.'
'Look at all this stuff we throw away!' Judy said. 'Did you know that one person throws away more than eight pounds of garbage a day?'

Do you know the third 'R' word?

'We recycle all our glass and cans,' said Mum.

'And newspapers,' Dad said.

'But what about this?' said Judy, picking a plastic bag out of the trash. 'This bread bag could be a purse! Or carry a library book.'

'What's so great about eggshells?' asked Stink. 'And smelly old ground-up coffee?'

'You can use them to feed plants. Or make compost.' Just then, something in the trash caught her eye. A pile of Popsicle sticks? Judy pulled it out. 'Hey! *My Laura Ingalls Wilder* log cabin I made in second grade!'

'It looks like a glue museum to me,' said Stink.

'I'm sorry, Judy,' Mum said. 'I should have asked first, but we can't save everything, honey.'

'Recycle it!' said Stink. 'You could use it for kindling, to start a fire! Or break it down into toothpicks.'

'Not funny, Stink.'

'Judy, you're not even ready for school yet. Let's talk about this later,' said Dad. 'It's time to get dressed.'

It was no use. Nobody listened to her. Judy trudged upstairs, feeling like a sloth without a tree.

'I won't wear lipstick today if it'll make you feel better,' Mum called up the stairs.

'And I'll only drink half a cup of coffee,' Dad said, but Judy could hardly hear him over the grinding of the rainforest coffee beans.

Her family sure knew how to ruin a perfectly good Mr Rubbish mood. She put on her jeans and her Spotted Owl T-shirt. And to save water, she did not brush her teeth.

She clomped downstairs in a mad-at-your-whole-family mood.

'Here's your lunch,' said Mum.

'Mum! It's in a paper bag!'

'What's wrong with that?' Stink asked.

'Don't you get it?' said Judy. 'They cut down trees to make paper bags. Trees give shade. They help control global warming. We would die without trees. They make oxygen and help take dust and stuff out of the air.'

'Dust!' said Mum. 'Let's talk about cleaning your room if we're going to talk dust.'

'Mu-um!' How was she supposed to do important things like save trees if she couldn't even save her *family* tree?

That did it. Judy went straight to the garage and dug out her Sleeping Beauty lunch box from kindergarten.

'Are you really going to take that baby lunch box on the bus? Where the whole world can see?' asked Stink.

'I'm riding my bike today,' said Judy. 'To save energy.'

'See you at school then.' Stink waved his *paper bag* lunch at her. If only she could recycle her little brother.

'Go ahead. Be a tree hater,' called Judy. 'It's your funeral.'

Making the world a better place sure was complicated.

---

1. Judy tells us how much garbage people throw away each day. What does she say?
2. In what way did Mum and Dad offer to help?

3. Judy and her family live in America. Sometimes they use different names for things, e.g. 'flashlight' instead of 'torch'. Find other examples.
4. Do you think Stink is funny or annoying? Find examples.

5. Look at the list Judy writes in her notebook. Is it different from a list you would make?
6. Judy is the main character in this story. How would you describe her character?
7. Can you think of another title for this chapter?
8. What do you think of Judy's behaviour and how her parents reacted to it?

9. What and how would you recycle in school?
10. How is compost made and what is it used for?
11. Would you like to change the world? How?

MEGAN McDONALD
JUDY MOODY
Saves the World!
Illustrated by Peter H. Reynolds

Where is the Forest?

John Foster

Where is the forest?
cried the animals.
Where are the trees?

We needed the wood,
said the people.
Wood to make fires.
Wood to build houses.
We cut it down.

Where is the forest?
cried the animals.
Where are the trees?

We needed the land,
said the people.
Land for our cattle.
Land for our roads.
We cut it down.

Where is the forest?
cried the animals.
Where is our home?

Gone, whispered the wind.
Gone. Gone. Gone.

Jungles

1. What do you know about jungles? How many plants and animals can you identify in the illustration?
2. Scan each of the headings. What do you think you will find out from each section?

Where are jungles to be found?

Jungles are dense forests that grow in hot wet places. They are among the steamiest and stickiest places on Earth. Jungles are also known as rainforests because it rains there just about every day. Rainforests can be found in many continents including Africa, America, Asia and Australia. South America is the largest and wettest and South East Asia is the most mountainous. Africa has the smallest number of plants. Australia has more than 2,500 kinds of flowering plants. About three-quarters of these cannot be found anywhere else in the world.

Threats to the jungle

Rainforests are home to an amazing number of plants, animals, birds and insects. They are the world's richest natural environments but they are under serious threat. Some forests are burnt to clear the land for farms and mines. Many trees are cut down for their valuable timber. An area the size of 40 soccer pitches is disappearing every minute. Scientists are worried that some species will die before they can even be identified. Scientists now understand how important rainforests are to us. Some of our most common medicines such as aspirin and cough mixture are made from plants found there. If the rainforests continue to disappear, life-saving cures may be lost forever.

Plants of the jungle

Some jungle trees grow very tall. They look like enormous umbrellas as
their leaves spread out and form a thick roof or canopy at the top of the
rainforest. Many reach heights of 40 or 50 metres. That's more than eight
times the height of a two-storey house! Some huge flowering trees, like the
giant gum, grow up to 110 metres, reaching high above the canopy. Below
the canopy, many plants and flowers grow in the shade. Thousands of

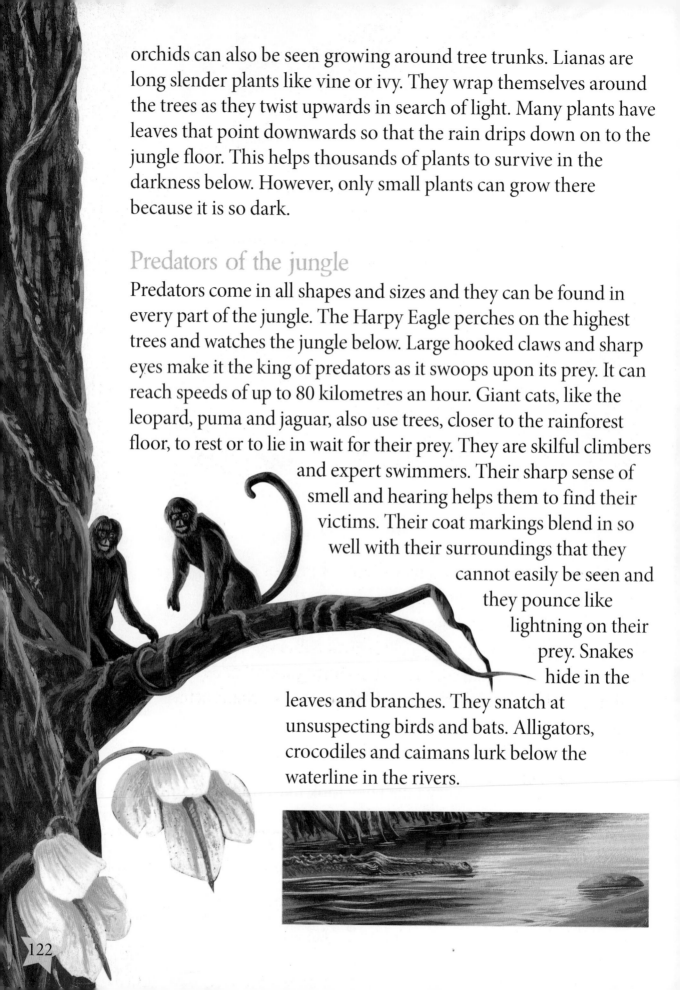

orchids can also be seen growing around tree trunks. Lianas are long slender plants like vine or ivy. They wrap themselves around the trees as they twist upwards in search of light. Many plants have leaves that point downwards so that the rain drips down on to the jungle floor. This helps thousands of plants to survive in the darkness below. However, only small plants can grow there because it is so dark.

Predators of the jungle

Predators come in all shapes and sizes and they can be found in every part of the jungle. The Harpy Eagle perches on the highest trees and watches the jungle below. Large hooked claws and sharp eyes make it the king of predators as it swoops upon its prey. It can reach speeds of up to 80 kilometres an hour. Giant cats, like the leopard, puma and jaguar, also use trees, closer to the rainforest floor, to rest or to lie in wait for their prey. They are skilful climbers and expert swimmers. Their sharp sense of smell and hearing helps them to find their victims. Their coat markings blend in so well with their surroundings that they cannot easily be seen and they pounce like lightning on their prey. Snakes hide in the leaves and branches. They snatch at unsuspecting birds and bats. Alligators, crocodiles and caimans lurk below the waterline in the rivers.

They feed on small animals, birds and fish. The bird-eating spider hides on the jungle floor and can kill its prey in one bite. The colourful but deadly pitcher plant releases a lovely scent. This attracts mini-beasts to the plant's slippery rim. They slide inside where they are slowly eaten.

Jungle acrobats

Jungles are also home to many different kinds of monkeys. They can be seen scampering along tree branches. They move skilfully like acrobats from tree to tree high up in the canopy. The howler monkeys of Central America have extra large voice boxes and make a loud booming sound at dawn and dusk. Their long thick tails are as strong as a man's arm. They use them to swing from tree to tree. Apes and gibbons have extra powerful curved hands. These help them to move quickly through the trees.

1. What words are used to describe rainforests?
2. Choose one of the animals or plants that you've read about and make a fact map about it. (See page 70).
3. Why are rainforests important?
4. Why are they disappearing?
5. Can you find some rainforests on a map of the world?

1. Read the introduction. Examine the pictures and make a prediction about what the story might be about.
2. Have you ever been to a zoo or held a wild animal? Talk about it.
3. What do you know about lions?

The Lion Cub

Eilís Dillon

Mark and his sister Catherine are visiting Dublin Zoo with their parents. They have already visited the monkey house and the snake house. Now they are on their way to look at the big cats.

Chapter one

At the lion house, Mark's mother said, 'Let's hurry through here.
They are lovely to look at, but they do smell awful.'
'They can't help it,' said Mark. 'It's their nature.'
'Well, it's my nature not to like it,' his mother said. 'One quick run through will do.'
It was true that there was a heavy smell in the lion house. No one wanted to stay there. As they came out, however, Mark's father met a friend. It was the old lion keeper, who had been there since Mark's father was a small boy, and who always recognised his visitors no matter what age they might happen to be.
'Mr Ward, glad to see you,' the keeper said. 'These your family? Want to show them some lion cubs?'
Immediately Mark knew that this was what he most wanted to see.
'Yes, yes,' he said. 'Where are they?'
'What's your name?' the keeper asked.
'Mark.'
'Then you're the man for lions,' said the keeper. 'I don't know why, but Saint

124

Mark is always represented by a lion. Called my own son Mark, for that reason, though he turned into an engineer afterwards. This way, please.' ⭐

He opened a door that led into another part of the building, at the back of the lion house. Inside there were more cages, most of them empty. One contained an animal no bigger than a cat, and very like a cat to look at except for its fierce yellow eyes. Its cage was padlocked and had double bars.

'That's a South American wildcat,' said the keeper. 'He has tetanus in his claws. One scratch from him would finish you. He'll spend six months in that cage and then he won't be dangerous any more.'

'What is tetanus?' Catherine asked. She always liked to understand everything. ⭐

'Blood poisoning,' said the keeper. 'He'll grow out of it. This way please.'

At the end of the room, in a cage that had no padlock at all, four lion cubs were playing together. They rolled over and over, holding each other's fur in their little teeth and growling ferociously. They were the size of the biggest cat that Mark had ever seen, and that belonged to Billy, the yardman, on the farm at home.

The keeper opened the cage, stepped inside and picked up two of the cubs.

'One each,' he said.

Mark took his and held it, stroking its woolly fur from head to tail. The cub began to purr. Mark and Catherine held the two cubs' heads together but they glared at each other and snarled on a high, angry, note, like cats at night. They took them away again.

'Mine likes me,' Mark said, when the cub licked his ear.

'He does too,' said the keeper. 'You have a way with lions, because of your name, I suppose.'

'I'll know this one always, wherever I see him,' said Mark.

His cub was darker than any of the others and had a dark-brown stripe on the top of his head.

⭐ What have you learned about the lion keeper?

⭐ What does this tell you about Catherine?

'Come back in a month or so and I'll let you take him for a walk on the leash,' the keeper said.

But Mark knew that with the harvest coming on, there would be no more trips to the zoo for a while. His father had said that this was the only time in summer when a farmer could have a little vacation. In the autumn there would be school, and then Christmas. By the time he would see this lion cub again, it would be as big as a calf. ⭐

After a while, the keeper took the cubs and put them back into the cage. 'Don't forget to come back,' he said to Mark.

'I won't forget,' Mark said. 'How could I?'

All the time they were spreading out their picnic lunch and eating it, Mark thought of the lion cub. He wanted to go away by himself to think about it, but of course this was not possible. When they had finished everything, his mother said, 'Who will take the bag back to the car?'

⭐ How do you think Mark feels at this point?

'I will,' Mark said instantly.

It was a big canvas bag that was always used for picnics. It was big enough for two families, which was a good thing when there were visitors. His father gave him the key of the station wagon and Mark started off, swinging the big bag by the handles.

At the lion house he paused. There was no one about. He looked quickly in every direction and then opened the door at the back of the building and slipped inside.

There was no one there either. Only the South American wildcat spat and hissed at him through its double bars.

The cubs were asleep in a warm, woolly heap in a corner of the cage. He opened the cage door and stepped into it. The cubs made no move. He put the bag on the floor of the cage and opened its neck wide. Then he picked up his own cub very carefully and laid it inside. He closed the zip fastener slowly, so as not to disturb the other cubs. None of them moved, nor even opened an eye to see what he was doing.

What do you think is going through Mark's mind?

He left the cage, closing the door quietly, and let himself out of the building. There was still no one around. The cub was heavy in the bag but he carried it high so that it would look rather empty if anyone were to wonder about it.

No one did. He passed through the entrance gates, where the ticket collector said, 'Had a good lunch? Feel nice and full?'

'Yes, thank you,' said Mark.

He opened the back of the station wagon and put the bag as near to the door as possible. He pressed the bag with his hand and thought he felt the cub warm inside.

'No noise on the way home, please,' he whispered. 'No growling, no purring.'

Then he locked the door again and went back to find the rest of the family.

1. Why was the South American wild cat kept apart from the other animals?
2. How was Mark's cub different from the other cubs?
3. Why did the lion keeper say to Mark, 'you are the man for the lions'?

4. Explain how Mark was able to take the lion cub without being seen.
5. Skim through the story and find words Eilís Dillon uses to describe the big cats.
6. The lion keeper is friendly towards the children. Find some examples of this.

7. Why did Mark decide to take the lion cub? Was it a good decision?
8. What kind of boy is Mark, do you think?
9. What do think will happen when Mark gets home?
10. Imagine that Mark's family makes him return the cub to the zoo. In groups, act out the conversation.

11. Have you ever done something on the spur of the moment? Talk about it.
12. When we think of St Mark we think of lions. What other saints do we link with animals?
13. What animal would you like to take home with you?

The Lion Cub
EILÍS DILLON
With Illustrations by Carol Bevers

The human body

1. Name parts of the body and talk about each one.

A baby has over 300 bones when it is born. An adult has only about 200 bones. Some of a child's bones grow together to become single bones. The smallest bone is in the ear.

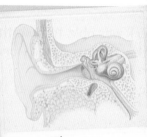

The ear

Nearly three-quarters of the human body is made of water.

The brain is the body's control centre. It sends messages to all parts of the body along the spine or backbone.

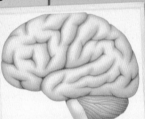

The brain

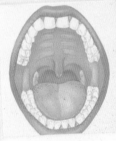

The tongue and mouth

There are about 9000 taste buds on your tongue. These allow you to tell the difference between sweet, bitter, sour and salty tastes.

Parts of the human body

The body is made up of billions of cells. Some cells live for only a few days. Others live for years. Bone cells last for up to twenty years but skins cells only last for about six weeks.

Your heart is like a big pump. It pumps blood to all parts of your body, bringing it the food and oxygen it needs to work properly. An adult's heart beats between 70 and 80 times a minute.

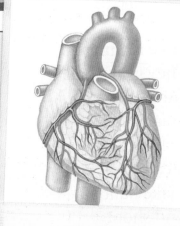

The heart

Your eyes move more than 10,000 times a day. It is very important to take good care of your eyes. Never look directly at the sun. When you are watching television, make sure that you don't sit too close to the television set.

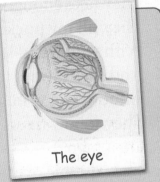

The eye

When you sneeze, air is expelled from your nose at a speed of up to 165 kilometres an hour. You should use a handkerchief if you are going to sneeze. Otherwise you will spread germs to the people around you.

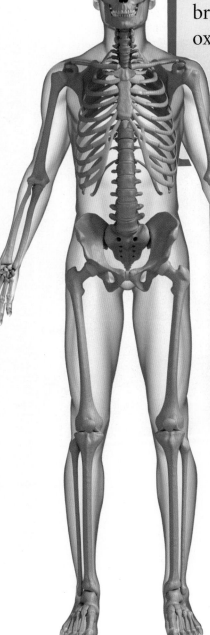

The human skeleton

1. How is the heart like a big pump?
2. How can you take care of your eyes?
3. What happens when you sneeze?
4. Why does an adult have fewer bones than a baby?

Mark's Fingers

Mary O'Neill

I like my fingers.
They grip a ball,
Turn a page,
Break a fall,
Help whistle
A call.
Shake hands
And shoot
Rubber bands.
When candy is offered
They take enough.
They fill my pockets
With wonderful stuff,
And they always tell me
Smooth from rough.
They follow rivers
On a map,
They double over
When I rap,
They smack together
When I clap.
They button buttons,
Tie shoelaces,
Open doors to
Brand-new places.
They shape and float
My paper ships,
Fasten paper to
Paper clips,
And carry ice cream
To my lips…

1. Read the introduction and look at the artwork. What do you think might happen in the story?
2. Have you read any books or seen any films about detectives or about people going missing? Talk about them.

Utterly Me, Clarice Bean

Lauren Child

Clarice and Betty Moody are best friends. They both love reading Ruby Redfort books. These books tell about the adventures of a rich young girl who is like a detective and has lots of amazing adventures. When their teacher Mrs Wilberton tells the class to do a project based on a book, the two girls decide to base theirs on Ruby Redfort. They even write a letter to the author. Then Betty mysteriously goes missing.

In class, some people are talking about their exhibits.

I am trying not to talk about mine because I am trying to keep it as top secret as possible because there might be copying from you-know-who, plus other people I could mention.

If only Betty Moody was here I could talk top secretly to her.

But she is off from school again.

No one knows where.

Grace Grapello hasn't heard my idea yet because she was luckily away when I came up with it.

I know what Bridget Garnett is doing – just the sort of project Mrs Wilberton would like. She has chosen a book called *The Wonderful World of Oz* about Australia.

Her exhibit is going to be kangaroos and their habits.

She says she is going to spend the whole day hopping, just to see what it feels like.

Andrew Hickley is doing the same, but with wallabies.

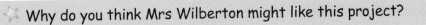

Why do you think Mrs Wilberton might like this project?

133

After lunch, I am getting even more fed up with Mrs Wilberton than usual.

She says my spelling is a bit here and there, and it's interesting how I can spell the same word so many different ways.

She says, 'Keep guessing and the probability is one day you will be right.'

I wish I had my old teacher, Mrs Nesbit. She was really nice and she would say 'well done' just for even slightly trying.

Nowadays trying your hardest just isn't enough for some people I could mention beginning with W.

Dad always says I should just try and stay out of her way.

What I want to know is HOW, when I am in her class every single day?

I wish I was grown up.

Dad says, 'It doesn't get any easier. You still have someone bossing you around.'

He says he finds Mr Thorncliff, his boss, very tricky and he tries to steer clear of him as much as possible.

I say, 'At least you get paid to be bossed around. I get bossed around for free.'

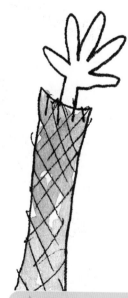

I can't concentrate because I am busy imagining Mrs Wilberton as a hippopotamus, and I am writing:

Mrs Wilberton is a hippipotimis

Mrs Wilberton is a hippipotimis

over and over again, without really meaning to. And what I am unaware of is that Mrs Wilberton is standing behind me, reading it.

She says, 'Can anyone here correctly spell the word

hippopotamus for Clarice Bean?' Of course, Robert Granger puts his hand up which is a joke because he is the last person who would be able to spell hippopotamus.

Luckily for me, Mrs Marse comes trotting in.

Mrs Marse looks a little bit like a hedgehog in high heels. She says, 'Can Clarice Bean please come to the secretary's office where there is a waiting mother.'

Everyone looks at me leaving because they know I must have something really important going on since I am going to miss half of an afternoon of Mrs Wilberton being dreary.

Mum is walking very fast across the playground, and I have to almost run to keep up.

When I get into the car, Minal is there chatting to himself like a twit.

Mum says, 'Sorry to drag you out of class early but you would not believe the morning I have had! There will be no one at home to let you in after school so you are just going to have to come with me.'

She says, 'If it's not one thing, it's a-blimming-nother.'

I say, 'Where is Grandad? Why isn't he at home?' Mum says, 'Grandad has got himself into some very deep water.'

It turns out that he has been banned from visiting his best friend called Bert-the-Shirt Finch at the Evergreens Old People's Home. And that Bert-the-Shirt Finch might be actually asked to please move out of Evergreens as he obviously cannot behave like a responsible senior citizen and abide by other people's rules.

Until the week before last, he lived in his own flat with a Pekinese and an Alsatian, but the people in the know said he wasn't

Why do you think Clarice's Mum has called for her?

What does to 'get into some very deep water' mean?

135

managing the stairs so well and what with one thing and another he had to be moved into an aged person's home with round-the-clock supervision. It was for his

own good.

Bert said he didn't mind moving and that it would be nice to get his meals cooked for him. Since the only thing he was eating before was cheese on toast and sometimes just cheese on nothing.

But the slightly big problem is Evergreen Old Folk's Home is strictly no dogs allowed and absolutely no cats either.

You may have a budgie. ⭐

Mum says, 'Everyone thought Bert had given his dogs to Mrs Cartwell.'

But, oh no, a certain person called Grandad has been keeping Flossie in the shed down the garden and the Pekinese called Ralph in his actual room and every night he has been smuggling them into Bert's bedroom at the Evergreens.

And every morning he collects them and brings them home.

Unfortunately, Ralph escaped and chewed Mrs Perkins' budgie, Oliver, until he was actually dead.

And Mrs Perkins has lodged a complaint against Grandad and Bert, and Mum is left to pick up the pieces.

We have to wait in the corridor while Mum sorts things out for Bert and tries to get him in somewhere else where you CAN have a pet.

Which is easier said than done.

Bert doesn't have a family, except for a long lost son in Alaska, and Mum says someone's got to come to the rescue.

⭐ **Why do you think budgies are allowed in the Home?**

Minal manages to spend one hour pretending to drive a toilet-roll car round the carpet. Thank goodness I have my book.

Ruby Redfort arrived back home after a long, hard day at school. Kicking off her shoes she ran upstairs to the kitchen.

Mrs Redfort was there, busying herself with whatever it was Mrs Redfort did, and Mr Redfort was reading the sporting pages.

Hitch was preparing elaborate fruit cocktails. Catching Ruby's eye, Hitch pointed discreetly at his watch. Ruby nodded.

Time was short – Hitch and Ruby were expected at headquarters at 1700 hours.

'Hi Mom, hi Dad! I just gotta go look at some history – you know, homework.'

'Of course my darling, I'm glad you are paying so much attention to your studies. What are you learning about these days?' enquired her mother.

'You know, stuff,' replied Ruby, evasively.

Luckily the telephone went, and Sabina Redfort became engrossed in a conversation about arranging cut flowers with Mrs Irshman.

'Quick Ruby!' whispered Hitch. 'We don't have much time. I need to get you to headquarters before...'

'Oh Ruby, sweetheart...' called out her father, but Ruby was already halfway up to her room.

'See you later, Dad. Gotta study!'

'But Ruby!' continued her father. 'Just to let you know, your mother and I would very much like it if you joined us for dinner this evening. Margorie and Freddy are coming over with their son, Quent. Supper will be served at eight. Ooh and sweetheart, wear something nice.'

'Darn,' sighed Ruby under her breath.

Apart from the nightmare of making it back in time, Quent was a real yawn. ✩

✩ How do you know that Ruby's family is very rich?

Mr and Mrs Redfort know nothing about Hitch's life as a secret agent helper. They have no idea that being a butler is just a sideline to him.

We get home and Kurt has cooked the supper for us.

It's not too bad actually. But I can't help noticing that he has been using a hairbrush on himself. Kurt doesn't have a hairbrush!
I bet he's been using mine, the weasel.
I am so busy thinking about this that I almost don't notice the letter, on the table, which is addressed to me with my name on it.
I open it straight away at once.
Inside there is a postcard of Patricia F Malpin Stacey in a trouser suit. It's the same picture as on the back of every single Ruby Redfort book.
The letter says:

Dear Betty and Clarace

Thank you for your kind enquiry. In answer to your question, the next Ruby book will be published this autumn.
The title is yet to be announced.

Patricia F Maplin Stacey hopes you continue to enjoy her books and wishes you happy reading!

Yours truly,
Patricia F Maplin Stacey

Creator of the Ruby Redfort Collection.

(Details of the fan club are listed on the Ruby Redfort website.)

I was hoping to get a slightly more helpful letter – it is not what I was expecting and I don't think Patricia F Maplin Stacey even wrote the letter herself.

It looked a bit typed and my name was spelt wrongly and I am sure Patricia F Maplin Stacey is a good speller.

When Dad hears all about Mum's dreadful day he says, 'It sounds like Grandad really is in the dog-house.' ⭐

Mum says, 'Right now, I do not find that remark one bit funny.'

I have the whole **weekend** to worry and wonder about what has happened to Betty Moody.

And the first thing I do is wake up at 7 o'clock on Saturday with my mind already thinking the worst.

One thought I had was that Mol and Cecil had sent Betty to boarding school because I have read about that happening to people in books when the parents get fed up with them.

But Cecil and Mol never get fed up with Betty – they utterly take her everywhere.

Also, Cecil and Mol have disappeared too, and no one is answering the phone, not even the answering machine itself.

Maybe the Moodys are on the run from the law, or maybe Cecil has invented an invention and someone wickedish is trying to steal it and the Moodys have had to go into hiding. Like in the book RUN FOR IT, RUBY.

Or maybe they have all been captured, and if they don't hand over the secret formula they will be dropped into a bubbling volcano, which is what happened to Ruby Redfort in WHERE IN THE WORLD ARE YOU, RUBY REDFORT?

In the story, it's up to Ruby's best friend, Clancy Crew, to solve the puzzle of the missing Ruby and follow all these clues. Clancy Crew is quite often having to do this.

Even in this book RUBY REDFORT RULES, I have got to this bit where Ruby seems to have disappeared, but don't worry, it's all part of her secret agent work. ⭐

⭐ Do you think this is funny?

⭐ What signs are there on this page that Clarice has an active imagination?

Clancy Crew tried to remember all the things Ruby had said during their telephone conversation just the other night. That had been the last time Clancy had heard from Ruby. Had Ruby been trying to tell him something?

Maybe she had been captured by some arch villain and was trying to let Clancy know her whereabouts in some sort of code. Now Clancy thought of it, it did seem strange that Ruby had mentioned that she was having tapioca pudding in China. Ruby Redfort hated tapioca pudding – everybody knew that! And just what was she doing in China?

In the story, Clancy does some quick thinking and works out tapioca stands for BAD NEWS (because tapioca is bad news if you don't like it) 'in' just stands for IN and China stands for

City **H**elp **I** **N**eed **A**dvice.

So the message is:

BAD NEWS. IN CITY. HELP! I NEED ADVICE...
It's so clever, I wish I knew code.

I get a sort of clue when I go downstairs.
It's come through the letter-box. It's a postcard with a picture of a strange, curly-shaped building on it and the words

Wish you were here!

The corner is torn off and I can't read who it is from.
Of course, it could be from Betty because there is a B and it is written in Betty's handwriting.
Maybe she is probably trying to tell me something...

but what?

1. What was Clarice writing in her copy?
2. Why was Clarice's Grandad and his friend in trouble at the Old People's Home?

3. How many people do you think are in Clarice's family? Can you name them?
4. How is Clarice's life different from Ruby Redfort's life?

5. What kind of person is Clarice's Dad? Why do you think this?
6. Would you like to have Mrs Wilberton as a teacher? Why?
7. How do you think Grandad's friend Bert will get on in the next Old People's Home?
8. Where do you think Betty might be?
9. Do you think Clarice is an easy child to teach? Why do you think this?
10. Look at the different kinds and sizes of print used. Why do you think the author presented the story like this?

11. Have you ever been taken out of school early? Talk about it.
12. What topic would you choose for a project?
13. Do you think old people should be allowed keep their pets in an Old People's Home? Give reasons for and against.

Utterly Me, Clarice Bean

Lauren Child

Crack the codes

1. What do you know about codes? Why do you think people use them?
2. Have you ever used a code? Talk about it.

Riddle of the Pharaohs

The people who lived in Egypt long ago were ruled by kings called Pharaohs. When the Pharaoh died he was buried in a huge tomb, called a pyramid. Many of the valuable treasures of the Pharaoh were buried with him. Sometimes even his servants were buried alive with him to keep him company on his journey to the next world.

People believed that the next world was a wonderful place and that those who reached it would live forever. But it was not easy to get to the next world. The Pharaoh first asked a ferryman to take him across a river. Then he had to fight snakes and crocodiles, and evil gods.

At the end of his journey, the Pharaoh had to face 43 judges. They weighed his heart against the feather of truth. If his heart was heavy with evil, the Pharaoh was punished by being devoured by a monster. If his heart was light, he would be saved.

People carved rows of pictures and symbols on the walls of the pyramids. This early kind of writing is called *hieroglyphics*.

Can you read the message that is written on this wall?

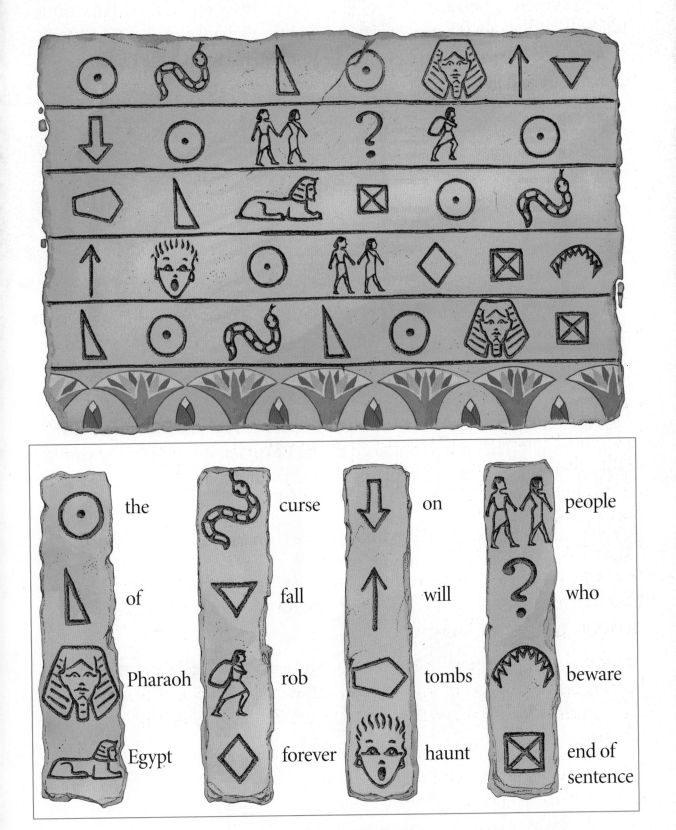

Key to the code

Ogham: an old Irish code

The Celts lived in Ireland long ago. They had their own special kind of writing. It was called *Ogham*. There were 20 letters in the Ogham alphabet. The letters were formed by making strokes on large stones. This is what the Ogham alphabet looked like.

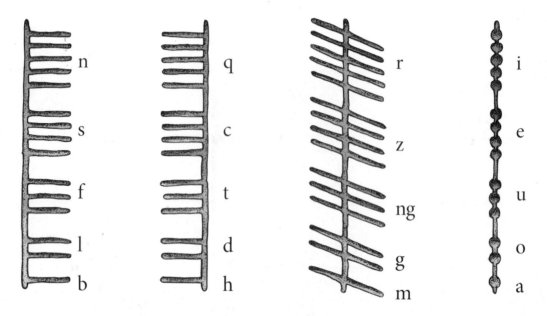

Ogham writing was read from the bottom up. It was carved on stones called Ogham stones. They often contained the names of famous people. Ogham stones can be seen in different places around Ireland today. Maybe there is one near where you live.

Can you crack the code and see whose name is on each stone? Remember that you must read from the bottom up.

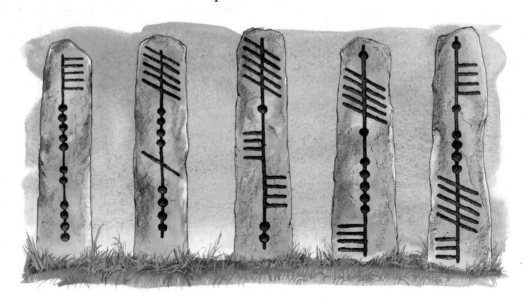

Bar codes

A modern bar code looks a bit like Ogham. It is a series of parallel lines and spaces that contain a lot of information. You have probably seen a bar code printed on packaging and labels. A bar code can be read by a laser scanner and the information is sent to a computer. Most supermarket checkouts use scanners.

A bar code like this can tell the computer many things, for example, the name of the product, its size and weight, and much more. A bar code is usually printed in black with a white or light colour background. The colour red can't be used in bar codes. Most lasers use a red light, so they can't pick up a reflection from red.

1. Can you write somebody's name in Ogham writing? Ask a friend if they can read it.
2. Talk about the differences between the Ogham alphabet and the alphabet we use today.
3. Find the bar code on this book. What information do you think it gives?

1. From the title, what do you think this story will be about?
2. What kind of character might Mr Gum be, do you think?
3. Scan the story. Look at the pictures and the different kinds of print used.
4. This story has lots of funny made-up words – keep an eye out for them!

You're a Bad Man, Mr Gum!

Andy Stanton

Chapter one: The Garden of Mr Gum

Mr Gum was a fierce old man with a red beard and two bloodshot eyes that stared out at you like an octopus curled up in a bad cave. He was a complete horror who hated children, animals, fun and corn on the cob. What he liked was snoozing in bed all day, being lonely and scowling at things.

He slept and scowled and picked his nose and ate it. Most of the townsfolk of Lamonic Bibber avoided him and the children were terrified of him. Their mothers would say, 'Go to bed when I tell you to or Mr Gum will come and shout at your toys and leave slime on your books!' That usually did the trick.

Mr Gum lived in a great big house in the middle of town. Actually it wasn't that great, because he had turned it into a disgusting pigsty. The rooms were filled with junk and pizza boxes. Empty milk bottles lay around like wounded soldiers in a war against milk, and there were old newspapers from years and years ago with headlines like…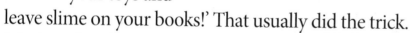

★ What are your first impressions of Mr Gum?

VIKINGS INVADE BRITAIN

and

WORLD'S FIRST NEWSPAPER INVENTED TODAY. ⭐

Insects lived in the kitchen cupboards, not just small insects but great big ones with faces and names and jobs.

Mr Gum's bedroom was absolutely grimsters. The wardrobe contained so much mould and old cheese that there was hardly any room for his moth-eaten clothes, and the bed was never made. (I don't mean that the duvet was never put back on the bed, I mean the bed had never even been MADE. Mr Gum hadn't gone to the bother of assembling it. He had just chucked all the bits of wood on the floor and dumped a mattress on top.) There was broken glass in the windows and the ancient carpet was the colour of unhappiness and smelt like a toilet. Anyway, I could be here all day going on about Mr Gum's house but I think you've got the idea. Mr Gum was an absolute lazer who couldn't be bothered with niceness and tidying and brushing his teeth, or anyone else's teeth for that matter.

(and as you can see, it's a big but) he was always extremely careful to keep his garden tidy. In fact, Mr Gum kept his garden so tidy that it was the *prettiest, greeniest, floweriest, gardeniest* garden in the whole Lamonic Bibber. Here's how amazing it was:

⭐ Why do you think the author chose these headlines? Was he being serious?

Think of a number
between one and ten.

Multiply that
number by five.

Add on three
hundred and fifty.

Take away eleven.

Throw all those
numbers away.

Now think of an
amazing garden.

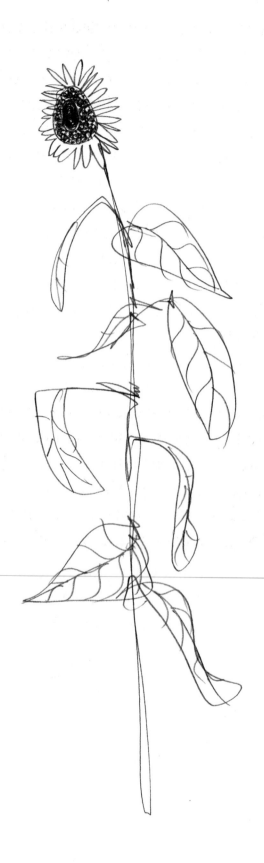

148

Whatever number you started with, you should now be thinking of an amazing garden. And that's how amazing Mr Gum's garden was. In spring it was bursting with crocuses and daffodils. In summer there were roses, sunflowers, and those little blue ones, what are they called again? You know, those blue ones, they look a bit like dinosaurs – anyway, there were tons of them. In autumn the leaves from the big oak tree covered the lawn, turning it gold like a gigantic leafy robot. In winter, it was winter. ✦

No one in town could understand how Mr Gum's garden could be so *pretty*, *greeny*, *flowery* and *gardeny* when his house was such a filthy tip.

'Maybe he just likes gardening,' said Jonathan Ripples, the fattest man in town.

'Perhaps he's trying to win a garden contest,' said a little girl called Peter.

'I reckon he just quite likes gardening,' said Martin Launderette, who ran the launderette.

'Oy, that was my idea!' said Jonathan Ripples.

'No, it wasn't,' said Martin Launderette. 'You can't prove it, fatso.'

In fact, they were all wrong. The real reason was this: Mr Gum had to keep the garden tidy because otherwise an angry fairy would appear in his bathtub and start whacking him with a frying pan. (You see, there is always a simple explanation for things.) Mr Gum hated the fairy but he couldn't work out how to get rid of it, so his only choice was to do the gardening or it was pan-whacks. And so life went on in the peaceful town of Lamonic Bibber.

✦ Is the writer having fun with the reader? In what way?

Everyone got on with their business and Mr Gum snoozed the days away in his dirty house and did lots of gardening he didn't want to do. And nothing much ever happened, and the sun went down over the mountains.

(Sorry, I nearly forgot. Something did happen once, that's what this story's about. I do apologise. Right, what was it?
Um...
Oh, of course! How could I be so stupid? It was that massive whopper of a dog. How on earth could I forget about him? Right, then.)
One day a massive whopper of a dog –
(Actually, I think we'd better have a new chapter. Sorry about all this, everyone.)

1. Name the town where Mr Gum lived.
2. Why did Mr Gum keep his garden so tidy?

3. List the things Mr Gum a.) hated b.) liked.
4. Picture Mr Gum's house. Which words from the story helped you?
5. How does the writer describe the changing seasons in the garden?
6. In the story the writer talks directly to the reader at times. Find examples of this.
7. The author uses some unusual descriptions. Find some and say what you think of them.

8. What other headlines might be found in Mr Gum's newspapers?
9. Would you like to live next door to Mr Gum? Why?
10. Were there any parts of the story that made you laugh? Talk about them.
11. What do you think might happen in chapter two? Give it a title.

12. Do you notice changes in your garden at different times of the year?
13. Many flowers are mentioned in the story. Name other flowers you know.

Acknowledgements

Fiction

The Little Boy's Secret from *The Book of Giant Stories* by David L. Harrison, Copyright © 2001 by David L. Harrison and Philippe Fox. Published by Boyds Mills Press. Reprinted by permission.

Extract from *Horrid Henry* by Francesca Simon, illustrated by Tony Ross. Reproduced by kind permission of Orion Children's Books, London. Text Copyright © Francesca Simon 1994. Illustrations Copyright ©Tony Ross 1994.

Sunkaissa, the Golden-haired Princess from SOUTH & NORTH, EAST & WEST, edited by Michael Rosen, illustrated by individual illustrators. Edited Text © 1992 Michael Rosen. Cover Illustration © 2007 Christopher Corr. Reproduced by permission of Walker Books Ltd, London SE11 5HJ www.walker.co.uk. Originally illustrated by Graham Percy. This illustration by Gill & Macmillan and not from original publication.

Extract from *The Whales' Song* by Dyan Sheldon, illustrated by Gary Blythe, published by Red Fox. Reprinted by permission of The Random House Group Ltd.

Extract from *Tiger Lily: A Heroine in the Making.* Text © Maeve Friel; illustrations © Joelle Driedemy. Published by Stripes Publishing, 2007. Reprinted by permission.

Extract from THE GIGGLER TREATMENT by Roddy Doyle. Scholastic Inc./Arthur A. Levine Books. Text copyright © 2000 by Roddy Doyle. Cover illustrations copyright © Charlie Fuge, 2000. Reprinted by permission. All rights reserved.

Extract from *The Pain and the Great One: Soupy Saturdays* by Judy Blume, illustrated by Kate Pankhurst, published by Macmillan Children's Books, London, UK. Reprinted by permission.

Extract from *The Winter Hedgehog* by Ann and Reg Cartwright, published by Red Fox. Reprinted by permission of The Random House Group Ltd.

Dino Egg by Charlie James © 2008, published by Bloomsbury Publishing Plc.

Extract from *Specky Becky Bucks* by John Quinn. Published by Poolbeg Press Ltd.

Chapter 1 from THE LEGEND OF THE WORST BOY IN THE WORLD by Eoin Colfer (Puffin 2007). Copyright © Eoin Colfer, 2007. Cover reproduced by permission of Penguin Books Ltd. Illustrations reproduced by kind permission of the illustrator, Tony Ross.

Extract from JUDY MOODY SAVES THE WORLD by Megan McDonald and illustrated by Peter H. Reynolds. Text © 2001 Megan McDonald. Illustrations © 2001 Peter H. Reynolds. Judy Moody font © 2001 Peter H. Reynolds. Judy MoodyTM. Judy Moody is a registered trademark of Candlewick Press Inc., Somerville MA. Reproduced by permission of Walker Books Ltd, London SE11 5HJ. www.walker.co.uk

The Lion Cub copyright Eilís Dillon 1966. Reproduced by permission of the Estate of Eilís Dillon.

Utterly Me, Clarice Bean by Lauren Child, published by Orchard Books. Reprinted by permission of David Higham Associates. Cover illustration reprinted by permission of Hachette Children's Books.

Extract from *You're a Bad Man, Mr Gum!* by Andy Stanton and illustrated by David Tazzyman. Text copyright © Andy Stanton, 2006. Illustrations copyright © David Tazzyman, 2006. Published by Egmont UK and used with permission.

Drama

Real Dragons Roar by Jacquie Buttriss and Ann Callander, from *Literary World Fiction Stage 2 The Alien and Other Plays* used by permission of Pearson Education Limited.

Poetry

'My Baby Brother's Secrets', 'The Wild Wind', 'What is Fog?' and 'Where is the Forest?' copyright © John Foster 2007 from *The Poetry Chest* (Oxford University Press), included by permission of the author.

'At My Birthday Party' by Anthony Browne reprinted by permission of the author.

'Happy Dogday' by Peter Dixon included by permission of the author.

'The Great Blue Whale' by Kerry Hardie, taken from *Something beginning with P* (O'Brien Press 2004), reprinted by kind permission of the author.

'The Whales' Hymn' © Brian Patten, first published in *Gargling With Jelly*, Puffin Books, 1985.

'Roger the Dog' by Ted Hughes, taken from *Collected Poems* by Ted Hughes, reprinted by permission of Faber and Faber Ltd.

'Oh, Woe Ith Me!' © 2001 by Bruce Lansky. Reprinted from *My Dog Ate My Homework!* With the permission of Meadowbrook Press.

'The Dinosaur's Dinner' by June Crebbin reprinted by kind permission of the author.

'Allosaurus' by Jack Prelutsky. Text © 1988 by Jack Prelutsky. Used by permission of HarperCollins Publishers.

'Mark's Fingers' by Mary O'Neill, reprinted by permission of ICM talent on behalf of the author.

The publishers have made every effort to contact copyright holders but any omission will be rectified at the next reprint.

Picture Credits

For permission to reproduce photographs, the authors and publisher gratefully acknowledge the following:

© Alamy: 35T, 43TL, 43BR, 44T, 44B, 52 second from top, 52 bottom left, 52 third from bottom left, 53 second from top, 53 third from bottom, 53 bottom left, 53 third from top, 52 second from bottom left, 53 third from top, 53 second from bottom left, 52 top, 52 second from bottom, 52 bottom right, 53 top, 53 fourth from bottom, 68T, 69C, 69B, 70, 84BL, 85CR, 85BL, 85BR, 86CR, 86C, 86CL, 86BL, 87TR, 87CR, 87BL, 87BCR, 96TR, 107, 109, 142; © Getty Images: 32T, 32B, 33TR, 33CL, 33BR, 34B, 35C, 68C, 69T, 73C, 76T, 84TR, 84CL, 84BR, 85TL, 85CL, 86TR, 86TL, 86BCL, 86BCR, 86BR, 87TL, 87CL, 87BCL, 87BR, 95T, 95BL, 96BR, 97T, 97C, 97B, 98CL, 98R, 98TL, 99T, 99CR, 99CL, 99BR, 108, 130TC, 130C, 131CR, 131L, 131TR, 130BL, 145; © Photolibrary: 85TR; © Science Photo Library: 34T, 34C, 84TL, 95BR, 96CL, 130R; © William Murphy/infomatique: 73.

The authors and publisher have made every effort to trace all copyright holders, but if any has been inadvertently overlooked we would be pleased to make the necessary arrangement at the first opportunity.

Art Credits

On behalf of MSM Studios: Monika Suska, Wojciech Kuzmiński, Aleksander Panek, Michał Nowak, Marta Handschke, Jona Jung, Dorota Łoskot-Cichocka, Agnieszka Stankiewicz, Jadwiga Żelazny, Ewa Zabaryło-Duma, Daria Brzezińska.